DATE DUE

MAR 1 3 1996	

PIONEER PLASTIC

PIONEER PLASTIC

The Making and Selling
of Celluloid

Robert Friedel

THE UNIVERSITY OF WISCONSIN PRESS

Published 1983

The University of Wisconsin Press
114 North Murray Street
Madison, Wisconsin 53715

The University of Wisconsin Press, Ltd.
1 Gower Street
London WC1E 6HA, England

First printing

Printed in the United States of America

For LC CIP information see the colophon

ISBN 0-299-09170-8

To my mother and father
and to the memory
of my brother, Howard

Contents

List of Figures

List of Tables

Acknowledgments

THE STUDY of history is a series of intellectual adventures, and so it seems fitting that I begin these acknowledgments with thanks to those who were most responsible for leading me into these adventures, even if they had little direct hand in this particular one: A. Hunter Dupree, A. Rupert and Marie Boas Hall, Jonathan Hughes, Eric Jones, and all my colleagues at the John Hopkins University.

All of the individuals and institutions that assisted in the completion of this work are too numerous to name, but it would be unthinkable not to acknowledge and give thanks to at least some of them. For their encouragment and good advice at crucial stages in this work, I must thank J. Harry DuBois, Reese V. Jenkins, Morris Kaufman, and Jeffrey L. Meikle. Valuable help was rendered by Mary Ann Bury and Harriet Raymond Stemmler of the Celanese Corporation and Helen Login of the Free Public Library, Millburn, New Jersey. The staffs of the Columbia University Library, the Eleutherian Mills Historical Library, and the Legal Records Division of the Washington National Records Center of the National Archives have given courteous and efficient assistance, often with a measure of added enthusiasm well beyond the call of duty.

Most of the research and writing of this work was completed while I was a Research Fellow at the National Museum of History and Technology (now National Museum of American History), Smithsonian Institution. The adventure recorded here would have been a far less exciting and satisfying one without the people and resources of one of the world's most wonderful museums. One of the great joys of studying the history of the first plastics was the opportunity that it gave for exploring the resources in half-a-dozen of the museum's divisions. My heartfelt thanks for patience and good humor as well as generously extended expertise go to the staffs of the following curatorial divisions of the Museum of History and Technology: Costume and Furnishings, Electricity and

Modern Physics, Medical Sciences, Photographic History, Preindustrial Cultural History, and Musical Instruments. Special thanks go to my host division, Physical Sciences, and its Curator of Chemistry, Jon Eklund, who steered me in the direction of celluloid in the first place. Other units of the museum, notably the History and Technology Branch Library and the Warshaw Collection of Business Americana, provided indispensable assistance along the way. Of the numerous individuals at the museum whose assistance went beyond their ordinary obligations, I would like to give special thanks to George Norton, Joanna Kofron, Margaret Sone, Susan Frey, and Robert Multhauf.

For his steadfast encouragement and friendship, in this as well as other enterprises, I thank William Coleman, of the University of Wisconsin-Madison. My gratitude is also extended to the Institute of Electrical and Electronics Engineers, my current employers, for their sympathetic understanding of the demands of scholarship, and to the University of Wisconsin Press, its editorial staff and its readers, for their expert guidance and wise judgment, as well as their patience. Finally, the last thanks — but far from the least — go to my wife, Toby Appel, for her ever faithful help, criticism, and encouragement.

Introduction

A Material and
Its Meaning

PLASTICS. The very word conjures up images in the mind that are both complex and evocative. As a derogatory term, "plastics" refers to those parts of our culture that are cheap, disposable, and undependable. In the realm of style, the word is associated with design that emphasizes smooth, flowing lines and either bold colors or glasslike transparency. Despite representing an enormously varied class of materials, "plastics" commonly evokes expectations of behavior within a fairly narrow range, including lightness, color-fastness, moisture-resistance, and flexibility. Above all, perhaps, "plastics" carries the meaning of "unnatural"—the epitome of the artificial or synthetic, whether applied literally to the materials of which things are made or figuratively to the artifacts or activities of our culture. Certainly few other substances carry with them the kind of symbolic meanings that are associated with plastics.

The sources of these meanings lie in part in everyday experience. If plastics did not actually behave in ways consistent with our feelings about the material or if they were not often used for the purposes that we commonly associate with them, even the most firmly entrenched images would not be long sustained in the popular mind. The fact is that eating implements or containers made of plastic *are* usually cheap and disposable; furnishings *are* often brightly colored with smooth lines and finishes; objects *are* made waterproof or mar-resistant by housing them in plastic. Nonetheless, it is obvious that there is more at work here than simply the observations of everyday experience. Other materials behave in predictable and ordinary ways that people are generally familiar with, and yet they do not carry with them such a host of associations and values. Only the precious metals, particularly gold, have acquired similar symbolic baggage, but their associations, deeply rooted in culture and language, are less ambiguous and are the products of several millennia of use and experience. The plastics, on the other hand, have been with us for little more than a century, and their widespread technical and economic importance is an exclusively twentieth-century phenomenon.

xv

Despite their relatively brief history, plastics do owe their cultural status to their past. The origins of modern plastics are clear and easily delineated, for in the middle of the nineteenth century, the experiments and dabblings of a number of individuals resulted in the material we know as celluloid, whose properties and applications turned out to be unlike those of any earlier substance. The processes of inventing celluloid and then of making it into a technically and commercially useful material took several decades, and in that period emerged the associations and images that are now attached to the whole complex class of plastics—most of which are far different chemically and physically from celluloid. Celluloid thus ushered in the plastics age culturally as well as technically.

The revolutionary nature of celluloid is apparent only from the hindsight of a century of subsequent plastics technology. When it first appeared in the 1860s, it was greeted simply as one of a myriad of "useful additions to the arts" which nineteenth-century men had already come to expect in the normal course of things. Certainly celluloid was not seen in the same light as the triumphs of the age, such as the telegraph, the steam locomotive, or Bessemer steel. This was in part due to the fact that the processes for making celluloid were unspectacular adaptations of old methods of mixing and forming natural substances. It was also due to the applications of the material, which more often than not diminished celluloid's distinctiveness rather than called attention to it. Contributing not least to the quietness of plastics' debut was the simple fact that celluloid was always a relatively minor material in the scheme of things. At a time when industrialization had brought forth the capacity and the demand for producing materials such as iron, glass, or cotton in the millions of tons, celluloid output never exceeded some hundreds of tons. Only after it had been made and sold for two decades did uses for celluloid emerge that were dependent on the material; hence, its impact on other technologies or products was undramatic. As a result both of its appearance and its application, celluloid did not call attention to itself.

None of this detracts from the fact that celluloid did represent an innovation of great significance for the future. As the first material with the properties that we associate with plastics and yet manufactured entirely from nonplastic sources, celluloid was the forerunner of an enormous and important class of artificial substances. It was also one of the host of new materials that emerged as part of the dynamism of nineteenth-century technology. Perhaps the best known of these innovations were mild steel and vulcanized rubber, but more novel materials also appeared in the course of the century, and it is they that signified most for the technology of our own times. The new metals, such as aluminum or magnesium, and the plastics represented an expansion of material capabilities every bit as important as the expansion of energy capabilities represented by the steam engine in the eighteenth century. Just as the growing use of steam power and the widespread application of iron were the hallmarks of the Industrial Revolution and the technological mode that Patrick Geddes termed "paleotechnic," so were the lighter new materials, along with the new energy technologies of electricity and internal combustion, at the heart of the creation of a "neotechnics" in the twentieth century. The plastics, still so strongly associated with novelty and modernity, are a somewhat neglected but key element in the creation of a neotechnic culture.

A look at the invention and exploitation of celluloid not only provides a better glimpse of the roots of twentieth-century technology, but it also presents special opportunities for understanding the nature of the technological dynamism that has propelled us through almost two centuries of revolutionary change. The creation of new materials raises important questions concerning the motivations for inventions, the means by which they are perfected, and the processes by which they are integrated into our culture. New machines tend to be obvious improvements in older ways of doing things; new materials, on the other hand, are often not obvious improvements in anything. They present novel combinations of properties whose functions may be quite unknown at first. Nonetheless, uncertainty about technical or economic value did not deter the development of new materials in the nineteenth century. Clearly, the creation of these materials put extraordinary pressures upon inventors and entrepreneurs to find important applications and secure markets in an environment that was only beginning to adjust to novelty as part of the expected order of things. The kind of responses evoked by these pressures gives us a clearer picture of the sources and consequences of technological innovation in the late nineteenth century.

This study is, therefore, to an extent a case history of technological innovation, after the manner of such well-known efforts as Donald Cardwell's study of the steam engine or Hugh Aitken's work on radio. No general model for technological change is proposed here, for the experience of celluloid is simply too narrow a base on which to build any kind of theoretical structure. Still, so basic are the issues involved in celluloid's early history that it is reasonable to suggest that conclusions reached here are relevant to anyone trying to reach a broader understanding of how new technologies emerge and how they are integrated into their economic and social milieu. The question that stirs Aitken, for example —how new things happen—is the question asked here too, but it is well to remind ourselves from the outset that the novelty and the creativity that are part of the introduction of a new technology are to be found not only in invention—the refinement of technical elements—but are also inherent in the adoption and exploitation of the technology. The story of celluloid brings this point home with special clarity, as we might expect in the case of a material so versatile and so novel.

This study is also an effort to remedy some of the past neglect of the early plastics by historians of technology. The emergence of new materials in the late nineteenth century has not been one of the classic subjects for historians' attention. This therefore leaves considerable room for simply providing a clearer picture of celluloid's invention and subsequent technical history. The creation of a useful plastic material from nitrated cellulose was not the achievement of a single man or a specific period of activity. The attempt began with the first successful production of nitrocellulose by a Swiss chemist and was not concluded until the inventions of an American printer more than twenty years later. Owing to the extended period and the multiplicity of independent efforts, the course of celluloid's invention is not a simple one to trace. But if the complications of celluloid's invention engender some confusion and uncertainty, they also provide valuable opportunities. The history of celluloid presents particularly clear examples of the problems, technical and otherwise, that must be confronted in creating a new material. The definition of celluloid—simply determining what it could and should be—was a difficult process, throwing light on the problem of defining any technology. The technical dimensions of this process were crucial; hence, due attention must be paid to the events of the invention itself.

The most significant issues in the history of celluloid, however, arise in the story of its application and impact. This story can be followed only against the background of the technological context in which celluloid was introduced. This context consisted most especially of those materials already in use in the mid-nineteenth century which had the properties of plastics. These "natural plastics" were relatively new, but by the time that work on nitrocellulose plastics began to make progress in the 1850s and 1860s, they were in widespread use. Their properties and the manner in which they were worked set the stage for the acceptance and the use of an artificial plastic. They did not, however, create the demand for such an invention. To the extent that such a demand preceded the invention of celluloid, it stemmed from experience with more precious, traditional substances, especially with ivory. The relationship between the introduction of celluloid and the status of these antecedent substances had an impact not only on the invention of the new material but also on the manner in which it was perceived and applied.

The search for applications for celluloid was actually a search for markets. It was clearly not enough to demonstrate that the new material could be used for various things. It was necessary to show that there were things for which it ought to be used. This effort included appeals to aesthetics, fashion, economics, and practicality. Celluloid met with many failures before securing stable and long-lasting markets. These failures are as instructive as the eventual successes, highlighting the uncertainty of celluloid's makers as to the proper images and functions of their product. The paths by which these images and functions were finally determined shed considerable light on the relations between perceptions of a new technology and real technical and economic needs. Eventually celluloid won a place for itself in a number of popular applications. The new technology established itself in traditional industries, sometimes with profound impact on these industries and the communities dependent upon them. The establishment of celluloid as a viable commodity reveals a great deal about the nineteenth-century response to new technologies, as well as about the accommodations made by inventors and entrepreneurs to the technological and economic environment around them.

During the twentieth century celluloid declined in importance. This decline was due largely to celluloid's replacement by newer plastics. Indeed, perhaps the most important result of celluloid's success was the fostering of the development of these more modern materials. By both its usefulness and its deficiencies, celluloid provided a model for the possible applications of plastics and for qualities to be sought and to be avoided in newly created materials. While celluloid was never the only useful plastic, it represented more than any other material the *idea* of plastics. The flourishing of this idea in the twentieth century was celluloid's most significant legacy.

It is not, however, the only legacy with which we live. The experiences of celluloid, caused by the nature of the material and of the markets into which it was introduced, have directly determined the social and cultural status of plastics in the twentieth century. Most especially, our association of plastics with the unnatural, the artificial, and the imitative can be clearly traced to celluloid. The way we think about our technologies determines how we use them and how we perceive their impact on us. Only when we begin to understand why we think about technologies the way we do can we hope to control them.

PIONEER PLASTIC

1

The Invention of Celluloid

THE INVENTION of celluloid was, like most inventions, a technical, economic, and social activity. At its foundation, however, it was a chemical activity, and therefore the understanding of the invention must begin with chemistry. To the twentieth-century chemist, celluloid is a solid solution of nitrocellulose and camphor.* Other materials were made throughout the last part of the nineteenth century and into the twentieth that were liquid solutions of nitrocellulose, solid compounds of nitrocellulose that lacked camphor, or cellulose plastics that were not nitrated. Only celluloid—and plastics called by other names because of trademark restrictions but otherwise identical—met all the qualifications of this definition. And it will be seen that the properties associated with these qualifications were of central importance to the technological and commercial role of the material.

"A Little Chemical Discovery"—Nitrocellulose

The essential source of celluloid was nitrocellulose. It was not until almost fifty years after the discovery of nitrocellulose that another soluble compound of cellulose (cellulose acetate) was manufactured. During this period (1845–1894) the properties of nitrocellulose were the subject of endless experiments and inventions. The two key properties of the material were explosibility and solubility. While these properties coexist in all forms of nitrocellulose, they predominate to different degrees depending on the extent to which the cellulose is nitrated. Highly nitrated cellulose is very explosive and, in the most nitrated forms, is largely insoluble in the ether-alcohol mixture that is the most important nitrocellulose solvent. Moderately nitrated cellulose, on the other hand, is

*In this work, the term *nitrocellulose* is used to refer to any form of nitrated cellulose, and no distinction is made between *nitrocellulose* and the more modern terminology *cellulose nitrate*.

3

not normally explosive and is almost totally soluble in ether-alcohol.[1] This more moderately nitrated form was known as pyroxylin; the highly explosive form, as guncotton.

In 1833 Henri Braconnot, a Frenchman noted for his experiments in animal and vegetable chemistry, investigated the effect of concentrated nitric acid on potato starch. The result was a nitrated starch which he named "xyloidine." Five years later Théophile-Jules Pelouze, also a French experimental chemist, investigated a similar reaction on paper and named the resulting nitrated cellulose "pyroxyline." Both xyloidine and pyroxyline were little more than laboratory curiosities, however, the fruits of the exciting first years of organic chemistry. Their composition was little understood and their properties, to the extent that the crude preparations available allowed any determination, were only dimly appreciated.

Despite the early French efforts, the credit for the discovery of, and the appreciation of, nitrocellulose is traditionally given to Christian Friedrich Schönbein, professor of chemistry at the University of Basel. In the course of experiments on oxidation (Schönbein is also famous for his identification of ozone), he undertook an investigation of the oxidizing properties of a mixture of nitric and sulphuric acids. While testing the effect of the acid mixture on organic materials, Schönbein reacted the mixture with cotton. The transformation of the cotton was startling. The product was hardly changed at all in appearance, but when brought near a flame, it burned violently. Schönbein quickly recognized the import of his discovery. On 11 March 1846, in Basel, he announced the discovery of guncotton and proposed its use as an explosive.[2]

The reason that Schönbein's discovery was more significant than those of Braconnot or Pelouze lay as much in his preparation as in his final product. The complete nitration of cellulose is largely impossible through the action of nitric acid alone. Another substance must be added to the reaction to take up the water released by what is, in essence, an alcohol-acid reaction, or else the nitric acid concentration quickly falls below the point where nitration can continue. Schönbein was aware of the importance of his nitric-sulphuric acid mixture and, in fact, refused to disclose his methods of preparation even when he announced his discovery. Despite his secrecy, however, other chemists soon succeeded in reproducing Schönbein's substance, and he felt compelled to try to patent his process. The first patent on guncotton was British Patent 11,407 of 1846, taken out for Schönbein by an agent.[3] American Patent 4,874 was issued to Schönbein himself in the same year.[4]

For Schönbein and the world at large the importance of guncotton was initially limited to its explosive properties. There was hardly a country in

Europe that did not, within months of the announcement of its discovery, form some sort of group to investigate the military possibilities of nitrocellulose. It required the work of forty years to develop a useful gunpowder out of nitrocellulose, although its use as a blasting powder, along with that of nitroglycerine, was less difficult to realize.[5] In the meantime, however, the other key property of nitrated cellulose, its solubility, had become the subject of widespread exploitation.

Moderately nitrated cellulose does not differ markedly in its appearance from the unnitrated form. However, when this material is mixed with any of a number of organic solvents, it goes into solution and loses completely its former texture and shape. More than a half-century of experiment revealed a multitude of nitrocellulose solvents—many of them proving to have important special applications. Much of the technical history of cellulose-based plastics is the history of the search for appropriate solvents. The first important one was a mixture of ether and alcohol* in various proportions—a fifty-fifty mixture being most popular. To this would be added moderately nitrated cellulose (pyroxylin) in proportions from 1 to 5 percent (and sometimes higher). The result of ths solution was a syrupy, colorless liquid. If applied to a surface and the solvent allowed to dry, this solution turned into a thin, transparent film or sheet of varying brittleness and strength. The idea of a plastic material made from nitrocellulose was inspired by this transparent film.

Schönbein himself observed the solubility of nitrocellulose in a mixture of ether and alcohol and suggested its possible value. The credit for the first public discussion of the uses of this solution, known as "collodion," is nevertheless generally given to a Boston medical student, J. Parker Maynard, who suggested its use as a "sticking plaster" which would provide a waterproof coating for wounds and surgical cuts. Maynard's first announcement of this application was in January 1847.[6]

Collodion was identified in the popular mind, however, not with surgery, but with photography. The long and important association of nitrocellulose with photography began in 1851 with the introduction of F. Scott Archer's "Collodion Process" or "Archerotype." While the use of collodion as a vehicle for photosensitive materials was suggested earlier by Gustav le Gray, Archer's wet plate process was the first practical alternative to the daguerreotype and albumen processes and was for better than twenty years the dominant photographic mode.[7]

While Schönbein himself was not clearly associated with the emerging applications of nitrocellulose in medicine and photography, there is

---

*Unless otherwise specified, *alcohol* in this work refers to ethyl alcohol. This was standard nineteenth-century usage.

evidence that he was sensitive to some of the novel applications to which his discoveries might lead. The directions in which Schönbein's thinking was running, even at the earliest stages of his nitrocellulose work, were remarkable anticipations of later events. In a letter directed to Michael Faraday, dated 27 February 1846, he announced: "I have of late also made a little chemical discovery which enables me to change *very suddenly*, *very easily* and *very cheaply* common paper in such a way, as to render that substance exceedingly strong and entirely waterproof."[8] A little later in the same letter, Schönbein promised Faraday that "before long you will hear of some other little chemical exploits I have of late performed; they consist principally in remarkable transformations of the most common vegetable substances."[9] This presaged Schönbein's next letter to Faraday, in which he announced the possibilities of his prepared paper: "To give you an idea of what may be made out of vegetable fibre, I send you a specimen of a transparent substance which I have prepared out of common paper. This matter is capable of being shaped out into all sorts of things and forms and I have made from it a number of beautiful vessels."[10]

It was in this same letter that Schönbein told of his discovery of an explosive cotton, but this news was given little attention compared to the transparent paper, which had electrical properties that Schönbein described to Faraday at some length. Schönbein also sent samples of his paper to J. C. Poggendorf, editor of the authoritative *Annalen der Physik und Chemie*, and Poggendorf responded with the suggestion that it might find use as a replacement for glass in windows or perhaps as a good material for bank notes.[11] Because of the dates of Schönbein's communications, the material in which he was so interested was probably not dried collodion. It was much more likely highly nitrated paper—a more nitrated form of Pelouze's "pyroxyline." It is nevertheless interesting that even at that premature stage nitrated cellulose was being investigated for its possibilities as a fabricative material.[12]

Alexander Parkes and Parkesine

While the manufacture and uses of collodion were well defined within a few years of its discovery, such was not the case with the plastic composition that was eventually developed from it. The production of a useful solid material made from nitrocellulose resulted from a slow evolution of concepts and techniques. Although the conjunction of nitrocellulose with the idea of a solid fabricative material with properties radically different from those natural to cellulose can be dated as far back as Schönbein's earliest experiments, it was quite different to come up with the third element of the concept of celluloid—the combined plasticizer-solvent, camphor.* This last, and crucial, step required twenty years of experimentation and false starts.

The history of serious efforts at developing a plastic material out of nitrocellulose began with Alexander Parkes (1813–90), a metallurgist, chemist, and inventor of Birmingham, England. At the age of thirteen Parkes was apprenticed as a "modeller and designer" to the firm of Samuel Messenger and Company, brassfounders of Birmingham.[13] Parkes's association with the plastic arts can be said to have begun here. Even at this early stage he was exposed to both the technical requirements of materials handling and the artistic sensibilities that accompanied fine craftsmanship. Upon completion of his apprenticeship, Parkes began work for another Birmingham firm, that of George and Henry Elkington, which in 1841 became Elkington and Mason, "electroplaters, copper smelters and silver smelters and general manufacturers of silver and german silver goods." Working for Elkington and Mason, Parkes styled himself as a modeller, manufacturer, and chemist. Beyond the main business of the company, he also occupied himself with "candle making, india rubber, chemical treatment of india rubber and gutta percha," and other activities.[14] Years later, when describing his work for Elkington and Mason, Parkes acknowledged the variety of experiments with novel materials and with novel ways of handling old ones that was sanctioned by his employers.[15]

Parkes's invention of a pyroxylin plastic was, he claimed, the product of many years' work, undertaken largely on his own. The result, which first appeared publicly in 1862, was dubbed (immodestly) "parkesine." This material varied in composition as efforts continued over the years to improve it, but it generally consisted of a mixture of pyroxylin and oils, with small amounts of organic solvents added to facilitate handling. Since its composition varied, parkesine's properties naturally varied as well. Those examples of the material that survive, however, are unmistakably plastic in appearance and feel, for parkesine could be easily colored and given a smooth, unblemished surface.† Parkes's first public discussion of his plastic was not given until 1865, but in that lecture he described at

*Camphor is a white, crystalline material extracted from the camphor laurel, a tree found almost exclusively in Taiwan. It has a complex bicyclic structure with the empirical formula $C_{10}H_{16}O$.

†Perhaps the earliest example of parkesine in the United States is a small piece of imitation malachite, now in the legal records of the National Archives, that Parkes submitted in a court deposition. Parkes claimed that this was a sample of the material he put on display in 1862.

length the history of his efforts and where he thought they had led him. At a meeting of the Society of Arts in London on 20 December 1865, the paper of the evening was a report by Parkes, "On the Properties of Parkesine and Its Application to the Arts and Manufactures." It was the most straightforward account of Parkes's work on his new material. Most striking was his attitude toward the need for a new substance:

> For more than twenty years the author entertained the idea that a new material might be introduced into the arts and manufactures, and in fact was much required; he succeeded in producing a substance partaking in a large degree of the properties of ivory, tortoise-shell, horn, hard wood, india rubber, gutta percha, &c., and which will, he believes, to a considerable extent, replace such materials, being capable of being worked with the same facility as metals and wood.[16]

"That a new material . . . was much required" and that it should combine "the properties of ivory, tortoise-shell, horn . . ." was a central tenet of the subsequent search for plastic materials. Parkes set the stage for that search by his attitudes as well as by his technical achievements.

Parkes's account was not rich in technical details, but he was clear enough on the materials he considered most important in the manufacture of parkesine: "Parkesine is made from pyroxyline and oil, alone or in combination with other substances; the various degrees of hardness or flexibility are obtained in the easiest and most expeditious manner by varying the proportions of pyroxyline, oil, and other ingredients."[17] He then went on to state vaguely that the pyroxylin used might be made "from any vegetable fibre" and that "the oils employed are some of the vegetable and some of the animal kingdom." While the paper at first glance appears to dwell on the technical aspects of parkesine's manufacture, Parkes was clearly unwilling to tell too much. It would be impossible to reconstruct Parkes's material from this discussion of it.

Parkes's account included a description of the origin of his interest in pyroxylin:

> The inventor, after much research, labour, and investigation, observed that the solid residue left on the evaporation of the solvent of photographic collodion produced a hard, horny, elastic, and waterproof substance. This led him to employ, in all his experiments, pyroxyline, xyloidin, or some collateral matter, as his base for future operations.[18]

Parkes was not the last inventor to be led on by that suggestive residue of hardened collodion.

In another section of his Society of Arts paper, Parkes indicated that he was aware, to some extent at least, of the utility of the material that was eventually crucial to the successful production of a pyroxylin plastic.

Another important improvement in the manufacture of parkesine is the employment of camphor, which exercises an advantageous influence on the dissolved pyroxyline, and renders it possible to make sheets, &c., with greater facility and more uniform texture, as it controls the contractile properties of the dissolved pyroxyline; camphor is used in varying proportions according to requirement, from 2 per cent. to 20 per cent.[19]

This was not the first mention of camphor in connection with nitrocellulose—that was probably in the patent of J. Cutting, of Boston, Massachusetts, for improvements in photographic collodion (British Patent 1,638 of 1854)—but it was the first hint of camphor's possible importance in producing a plastic material.

Parkes's understanding of the usefulness of camphor revealed a great deal about how he perceived the material he was making, for the properties of plasticity and stability that camphor imparts to celluloid are crucial to its integrity and usefulness. The question of Parkes's use of camphor was central to the patent litigation that dogged the American manufacturers from 1876 to 1884, when the basic U.S. patents on celluloid were challenged on the grounds of the early English work. In his first decision of the case, in May 1880, Judge Samuel Blatchford of the U.S. Circuit Court for the Southern District of New York stated that he could not find in the patents of Parkes or elsewhere anticipation of the use of camphor and alcohol as a solvent of pyroxylin.[20] Four years later, however, Judge Blatchford reversed himself and decided that Parkes's British patent 1,313 of 1865 did indeed cover the use of a camphor-alcohol mixture as a solvent in the manufacture of a pyroxylin plastic.[21] A great deal of the evidence available to Judge Blatchford can still be examined. The evidence presented by Parkes was an interesting reflection of the man's own ideas of his technical contributions.

Parkes's testimony before a U.S. commissioner in London in the summer of 1878 suggested that his knowledge of the possible uses of camphor was more extensive than elsewhere indicated. Under cross-examination, Parkes stated,

It is true that I used alcohol and camphor at that early date [1853] in my laboratory to the best of my knowledge—I am trusting to memory in all · these answers that I am giving and I believe that I was the first to discover the fact that alcohol alone was a solvent of nitrocellulose and I published that fact in my patent of the year 1855 and I also soon after discovered the fact that camphor alone was a solvent of nitrocellulose.[22]

A little later in cross-examination, this exchange took place:

Q: Will you swear that prior to leaving South Wales you had discovered the use of camphor and alcohol as a solvent of xyloidine [pyroxyline]?

A: Yes, I will —

Q: Will you also swear that you realized its value?

A: Certainly, I had been working for it a long time.[23]

Despite this unequivocal stance, it is more likely that Parkes had no real conception of the capabilities of camphor.[24] His patents, whenever they mentioned the material, mentioned it only in passing, and he never specified the use of camphor in the direct claims of his patents.[25]

In his testimony, Parkes insisted that a solvent consisting of "about equal parts of camphor and alcohol and in proportions ranging both ways higher and lower in both things" was used in the manufacture of parkesine, even before Daniel Spill took out his patent involving the use of camphor (British Patent 3,102 of 1869).[26] Yet, camphor was clearly not seen as a necessary ingredient of parkesine: a typical recipe consisted of "100 parts of pyroxylin, moistened with naphtha, 10–50 parts of nitrobenzole or aniline or camphor, 150–200 parts of vegetable oil."[27]

Parkes's 1865 article makes clear his early preoccupation with producing his product cheaply. He declared to the Society of Arts that he could produce "any quantity" (many tons per day) of parkesine for less than one shilling per pound. This economy (requiring "no less than twelve years' labour and an expenditure of many thousand pounds" to achieve) was effected by cheapening the materials of manufacture. Parkes devised means of producing nitrated cellulose from waste cotton, linen, and paper. He used special devices to recover the solvents of the pyroxylin and adopted cheaper solvents, such as wood naphtha.[28] The result of these efforts was a considerably cheapened product—one which turned out to be almost worthless in manufacturing. This was commented upon by Edward C. Worden, writing in 1911: "In order to produce tons, where perhaps they should have been contented at first to make pounds, the finished product was sent out without complete elimination of solvents, and with but little regard for uniformity. It is stated that combs sent out in a few weeks became so wrinkled and contorted as to be useless."[29] But Parkes's greatest technical error was, as Worden went on to say, the attempt to make his compound plastic by adding large amounts of castor oil. As long as Parkes's product contained oils as a plasticizer, it would never be a useful material. Indeed, this was one of the major reasons why the company founded in 1866 to manufacture and sell parkesine folded two years later.

Xylonite: Daniel Spill Continues

The story of the early English efforts to make a nitrocellulose plastic does not end, however, with the quick failure of Parkes's company. This first commercial venture brought into the history of celluloid another Englishman, Daniel Spill, who contributed more tenacity than technical knowledge to the development of a plastics industry. Spill, unlike Parkes, was not easily discouraged in his efforts to make a business success out of the new material, and his dogged pursuit of this goal for better than twenty years embroiled him in controversy that made his real contributions difficult to assess. Even years after his death, chemists could be found debating whether Spill ever really made celluloid and how much the industry ultimately owed him.[30] The story of Daniel Spill, however, is less interesting for the light it sheds on celluloid's technical history, than for what it reveals about the technical and economic uncertainties that surrounded the industry's beginnings.

Spill was born in Gloucestershire in 1832 and acquired training as a doctor.[31] He very early dropped this profession, however, and went to work for his brother George, who was by the 1850s successfully operating a factory for the production of waterproof cloth. The business of George Spill and Company, set up in East London, consisted of spreading rubber on cotton cloth, an enterprise which grew quite substantial with the military requirements for waterproof clothing arising out of the Crimean War. This preoccupation with waterproofing also provided the link between George Spill and Company and the inventions of Alexander Parkes.

When Parkes exhibited samples of parkesine at the London Exhibition of 1862, one of the prominent claims made for his material was its waterproofing qualities. A number of his patents suggested the use of a parkesine coating in waterproofing. Shortly after the Exhibition, Parkes was contacted by Spill's company regarding the use of his new material under license. Rather than licensing Spill, however, Parkes joined the company in an effort to develop the full range of commercial possibilities offered by parkesine. Thus, from 1864 on, Daniel Spill was deeply involved in attempts to solve the technical and commercial problems presented by the production and sale of parkesine.[32]

The precise extent to which Spill added to an understanding of the technical requirements of a successful plastic was an issue heatedly debated many years afterwards. Nonetheless, the limitations of Spill's contributions are clear. He was granted seven British patents related to what he called "xylonite."[33] Five of these concerned solvents, including camphor. Since it is clear that Alexander Parkes had some notion of the usefulness of camphor, the simple idea of combining pyroxylin and camphor cannot be attributed to Spill. Furthermore, Spill's only public essay on xylonite indicated that he had little better notion than Parkes of the real importance of camphor. In a paper read to the London Photographic

Society in December 1870, Spill gave some details on how he prepared his material:

> The solvents commonly employed in the preparation of photographic collodion are too expensive to permit of their use in the xylonite manufacture, and we have recourse to solvents, either fixed or volatile, or judicious mixtures of both these qualities, by which an almost endless variety of materials can be prepared. The volatile solvents mostly used are wood spirit, alcohol, aldehyde, mineral naphtha, benzole, and other hydrocarbons; and the nonvolatile or fixed solvents are oil and camphor, or natural camphor oil, linseed, castor, and other vegetable oils. The introduction of these fixed solvents is an important improvement and economy in the manufacture of xylonite, obviating much loss by evaporation and inconvenience arising from contraction of the material. To prepare these solvents take, say, 100 parts of castor oil and heat up to about 250° or 300° Fahr., then dissolve therein about fifty parts of camphor, and while in the heated condition add the xylodine, which readily dissolves into a stiff paste, and is then ready for a subsequent process.[34]

Spill never ceased advocating processes either with substantial amounts of added oils or excessive amounts of volatile solvents. Xylonite was not celluloid.

John Wesley Hyatt: The Celluloid Solution

The problem of the solvent was the key to producing a useful plastic material from nitrocellulose. The initial suggestion for a nitrocellulose plastic came from collodion, which, by its very nature, had a high solvent content. It thus required a substantial conceptual leap to get away from attempting to produce a plastic by evaporating the solvents from a liquid solution of nitrocellulose. The product of evaporated collodion was, even if produced carefully and under rigid conditions, a badly shrinking, often brittle film. The plasticity necessary for a moldable solid material could, to some extent, be imparted by the addition of substantial amounts of oils. But this too had to be done under special conditions and apparently produced products still subject to shrinkage and warping. The successful nitrocellulose plastic would have to be made with a nonvolatile solvent and an effective and cheap plasticizer.

Despite these difficulties, the attraction of applying nitrocellulose to uses as a plastic or a waterproofing was not confined to just a few experimenters. A list of patents was introduced during the litigation of the 1880s to show the broad scope of pyroxylin applications attempted even before Daniel Spill's 1869 patents. Aside from Parkes's, the British patents listed included those issued to James Cutting (1,638 of 1854), Louis Cornides (745 of 1855), Stephen Barnwell and Alexander Rollason

(945 of 1859 and 2,249 of 1860), and William E. Newton (536 of 1868).[35]
Cuttings's patent was related to photography, Cornides's to waterproofing paper, Barnwell and Rollason's to cement and paint. These were a
mere fraction of the British patents related to pyroxylin in the period between 1850 and 1870. Others were issued for coating fabrics, making artificial gums, coating hats and bonnets, imitation bearskin, varnishes and
lacquers, and collars and cuffs.[36]

American inventors were slower to get involved in the search for pyroxylin applications, but by the late 1860s they too had collected a lengthy
list of patents. In 1865, G. W. Ray took out a patent (U.S.P. 48,239) for
an "imitation linen collar of pyroxyl," and in 1867 U.S.P. 65,267 was
granted to William H. Pierson for an "improved plastic compound made
from vegetable fibers."[37] The latter patentee claimed to "have invented or
discovered a certain new and useful art—viz., the art of manufacturing
certain useful and ornamental articles out of plastic."[38] While the process
Pierson described was little more advanced than that of Parkes, his concept of a plastic material with a wide variety of forms and uses was as
clear an expression of the modern idea of plastics as the nineteenth century was to produce. In addition to Ray and Pierson, other U.S. patents
related to pyroxylin plastics were issued before John Wesley Hyatt's:
John McClelland received a patent (77,304) in 1868 for an "improved
material for dental plates"; Charles A. Seely received one the same year
for solidifying collodion (79,261); and L. R. Streeter was issued four
patents (88,228; 88,260; 89,253; and 89,254) in 1869 for various uses of
pyroxylin, including dental plates and other articles.[39] By the time Hyatt
took out his first patent for a pyroxylin plastic in 1869, the idea of such a
material was no longer novel.

John Wesley Hyatt was born in upstate New York in 1837. Son of a
blacksmith, Hyatt was trained as a printer and practiced that trade first
in Illinois and then in Albany, New York. In 1863, so the story goes,
Hyatt's attention was caught by the offer of a prize of $10,000 from the
firm of Phelan & Collender in New York City for the patent rights to a
substitute for ivory suitable for the manufacture of billiard balls. Attack-
ing the problem in a fairly conventional manner, Hyatt proceeded to
make up various well-known plastic compositions, such as a combination
of pressed wood pulp and gum shellac, then popular for making daguerreotype cases. While these materials did not produce a satisfactory
billiard ball, Hyatt did set up a company to use them for the manufacture
of small articles like checkers, dominoes, and so forth.[40]

An important result of Hyatt's work with these early plastic compositions was that he became familiar with processes for molding plastic compounds under heat and pressure. Parkes and Spill, to name the two most

important of Hyatt's predecessors, lacked such familiarity, at least when they began their work with pyroxylin.[41] These earlier workers thought more often in terms of making liquid collodion solid, rather than making the solid pyroxylin moldable. This was the most critical difference in the methodology of Hyatt. Hyatt's own description of how he approached the problem is the best one:

> From my earliest experiments in nitrocellulose, incited by accidentally finding a dried bit of collodion the size and thickness of my thumb nail, and by my very earnest efforts to find a substitute for ivory billiard balls, it was apparent that a semi-liquid solution of nitrocellulose, three-fourths of the bulk of which was a volatile liquid and the final solid from which was less than one-fourth the mass of the original mixture, was far from being adapted to the manufacture of solid articles, and that I must initially produce a solid solution by mechanical means.[42]

Hyatt received several patents in 1869. One was simply for improvements in molding pulp-shellac compositions, but two later patents involved the use of collodion or pyroxylin. The first of these, U.S.P. 88,634, was for applying coats of collodion to composition billiard balls, but the second, U.S.P. 91,341, was the earliest indication that Hyatt had seriously turned his attention to the problem of producing a pyroxylin plastic. This patent, for an "improved method of making solid collodion," was significant for the emphasis that it placed on the use of high pressures. It should be contrasted with a patent issued to Daniel Spill on the same day (U.S.P. 91,377: 15 June 1869) for "improvement in compounds containing xyloidine." While the Spill patent made prominent mention of the use of camphor, it also included the addition of oils. Hyatt's patent described a substance containing pyroxylin, a small amount of liquid solvent (such as ether), and solid fillers (ivory-dust, asbestos, or the like) which was molded under a pressure of between five and twenty tons per square inch. This would produce a material that was no more celluloid than Spill's product, but at least it did not contain oils and it was molded under the high pressures that would prove essential to celluloid.

Hyatt was aware of the earlier work on pyroxylin plastics that had uncovered the usefulness of camphor, as he himself indicated:

> Finding it stated in some patents to which I was referred, that a little camphor added to the liquid solvent was beneficial, we conceived the idea that it might be possible to mechanically mix solvents with the pulp and coloring matter while wet, then absorb the moisture by blotting papers under pressure, and finally submit the mass to heat and pressure.[43]

Out of the success of this experiment came the fundamental celluloid patent, U.S.P. 105,338 (12 July 1870), "Improvement in treating and molding pyroxyline." The process described by the patent called for first grinding pyroxylin in water until it was reduced to a fine pulp and then adding appropriate pigments or dyes. Next, while the pulp was still wet, there would be mixed with it "finely-pulverized gum-camphor in about the proportions of one part (by weight) of the camphor to two parts of the pyroxyline when in a dry state." After all water was removed from the pyroxylin-camphor mixture by pressing or straining, it was then placed in a mold, heated to 150°–300° F and then subjected to heavy pressure. The result of this is best described by the patent itself:

> The heat, according to the degree used, vaporizes or liquifies the camphor, and thus converts it into a solvent of the pyroxyline. By introducing the solvent in the manner here described, and using heat to make the solvent active, and pressure to force it into intimate contact [with] every particle of the pyroxyline, we are able to use a less proportion of this or any solvent which depends upon heat for its activity than has ever been known heretofore. After keeping the mixture under heat and pressure long enough to complete the solvent action throughout the mass it is cooled while still under pressure, and then taken out of the mold. The product is a solid about the consistency of sole-leather, but which subsequently becomes as hard as horn or bone by the evaporation of the camphor.

That Hyatt's perception of his process was influenced by the earlier efforts to use volatile solvents is apparent in his reference to the hardening of his product by evaporation of the camphor.[44] In truth, only the surface camphor, and with it the strong camphor odor, evaporated. The integrated camphor remained as an essential ingredient in the finished product. This product was celluloid, though the name was yet to come.

From Albany to Newark

John Wesley Hyatt, now joined by his brother, Isaiah Smith Hyatt, was apparently satisfied that the product of his nitrocellulose-camphor process was a material with substantial potential. Despite this, when the Hyatts tried to interest a hard-rubber manufacturer in the material, they were rebuffed and, to boot, told that their process—requiring, as it was perceived, heating guncotton under high pressure—was likely to blow them to bits. While some experimenting was done to demonstrate that the danger had been exaggerated, the initial process was nevertheless modified by adding small amounts of alcohol or some other solvent to the camphor before it was mixed with the pyroxylin. This lowered the temperature necessary to dissolve the pyroxylin, thus reducing the hazards of working with the highly inflammable nitrocellulose.[45] This seemingly small change in the process was necessary to make celluloid manufacture an acceptably safe activity, but it also muddied the distinction between Hyatt's manufacture and that of Spill or Parkes, for whom the use of a camphor-alcohol solvent for pyroxylin seemed to present no novelty at all.

Despite the fact that Hyatt's process, as it was actually carried out, bore a resemblance to formulae that had been tried by Parkes and Spill, Hyatt's product was different from the earlier materials, largely because of the effort made to keep the use of a volatile solvent to a minimum. Many years afterwards, in 1914, Hyatt summarized his innovations: (1) use of the solvent to produce a *solid* solution, (2) use of heat and pressure to complete the solution, (3) purification of the nitrated cellulose, (4) simplification of the nitration process (using tissue paper in place of carded fiber), (5) elimination of the need for drying out the finished product, and (6) the development of appropriate machinery for fabrication (especially "stuffing" and "sheeting" machines).[46] These developments did not come all at once, and each of them was characterized by differing degrees of novelty and of importance to celluloid technology. Clearly, however, the idea of the solid solution was the crucial one, and significantly, Hyatt described it without mentioning camphor.

Much of the success of celluloid was due to the further improvements Hyatt and his co-workers made in its manufacture. Hyatt's allusions to his improvements in the crude materials of pyroxylin manufacture reflected the importance of developing all fundamental aspects of plastics manufacture beyond the rudimentary levels achieved by earlier experimenters. Hence, safety improvements and innovations in molding and shaping the finished material were also significant. These technical achievements were not all accomplished when Hyatt's commercial ventures began, but there seems to have been, from the start, a recognition on the part of Hyatt and his backers of the importance of such on-going technical development if the enterprise was to succeed.

In 1870, Hyatt and his brother set up the Albany Dental Plate Company to manufacture dental plate blanks from their new material. For two years this was the primary article made of celluloid, and aided by dentists' antagonism towards the rubber trust, the new material found some acceptance. In this period Isaiah Smith Hyatt coined the name "celluloid," in recognition of the primary material from which the substance was made, cellulose. "Celluloid" was registered as a trademark in the U.S. Patent Office and its legal use in the United States was always restricted to the products of Hyatt's company and its successors. This did not, however, prevent the name from replacing all other names for pyroxylin plastics as far as the public was concerned, in the United States as well as abroad, where trademark restrictions did not apply. The coining of a euphonious and distinctive name for their product was another contribution to the success of Hyatt and his company.

The Hyatts' registration of a name for their invention demonstrated their faith in the potential of celluloid. On 28 January 1871, the Celluloid Manufacturing Company was organized in Albany with an initial capitalization of $60,000.00. The purpose of this company, which absorbed the dental plate operations, was to manufacture and sell celluloid in a semifinished form—in rods, sheets, tubes, etc. Further evidence of the expansion of celluloid manufacture came from the transfer of the operation from Albany to Newark, New Jersey, in late 1872. This followed the recruitment of capitalists and businessmen who were persuaded of the commercial possibilities of a dependable plastic material.[47] Less than two and one-half years after the basic celluloid patent had been issued to Hyatt, the industrial production of the material was permanently established and the creation of markets had begun.

Making Celluloid

From 1872, the history of celluloid is more the story of commercial enterprise than of technical development. Before looking at the marketing of celluloid, however, it would be useful to examine briefly the technology of celluloid production after it had emerged from the early period of experimentation. This technology actually changed very little in the several decades following Hyatt's original formulation. Indeed, the one important change from Hyatt's 1870 patent—the use of alcohol or a similar solvent to facilitate the solvent action of camphor—was one made by Hyatt himself shortly after he began production.[48]

While the first experimenters with pyroxylin plastics often procured their nitrated cellulose from other manufacturers, the need for careful control over the degree of nitration and the material quality of their product led most plastics manufacturers to begin producing their own nitrocellulose. This was normally made from tissue paper manufactured from cotton textile scraps and specially formulated for pyroxylin manufacture. The distinction between pyroxylin and the more heavily nitrated guncotton was understood fairly early. Plastics manufacturers developed formulae for making pyroxylin with the desired degree of nitration, and hence of solubility. This was achieved largely through variations in the proportions of nitric acid, sulphuric acid, water, and paper, as well as through variations in the time allotted for the nitration.

The nitrocellulose was then prepared for its ultimate union with camphor. After the nitration process and the washing out of the acids (a very important step for the stability of the final product), a high proportion of the pyroxylin was bleached. This was accomplished by the use of common bleaching agents such as chlorine bleach or potassium permanganate and was important for the production of clear plastic or the very popular ivory or white products. After the bleaching, or sometimes during it, the nitrated paper was converted into a pulpy mass by beating and grinding machines. If the product was to be colored, the dye or pigment would be added after the pulping was completed. This would be thoroughly mixed into the pulp, usually in the grinding process. Once this was done, the pyroxylin was ready for conversion.

Conversion consisted primarily of mixing the prepared pyroxylin with camphor. There appear to have been a number of methods used for this mixing, but the one favored by Hyatt consisted of grinding the moist pyroxylin for several hours with finely divided camphor, just enough moisture being added to aid smooth operation of the mixing machines. Following this, the "minimum" amount of solvent would be added to the mixture and the entire mass once again sent through a long process of grinding, mixing, and standing until the solvent was in intimate contact with all parts of the mass. Just as for many of the earlier procedures, there were special machines devised for this stage of production. Once this mixing had been completed, it was common for stabilizers to be added, largely to counteract the effects of any acid that might still remain in the mixture.

The final stage in manufacture began with drying of the pyroxylin-camphor mixture. All liquid was eliminated by pressing, blotting, and drying over a period of time that might stretch into several days. The resulting dry cakes were then broken up and a very small amount of alcohol sprayed onto the pieces. After a few hours of standing, the material would be pressed and masticated between heated rollers for up to an hour and then stripped from the rollers as semifinished celluloid. This was in turn either put into stuffing machines and forced out in desired shapes—tubes or rods—or pressed into blocks and planed or cut into strips or sheets. The finished celluloid was then usually seasoned for up to several months (depending on thickness) before being sent out to be made into a finished product.[49]

The manufacture of celluloid was not an especially complicated process, although the materials used did make it a hazardous one. As usually carried out, it required considerable capital equipment, largely machinery, and was hence subject to major economies of scale. The manufacture of raw celluloid was thus always concentrated in a few large factories, and its supply was in the hands of a few sizable companies. In the United States, for example, there were never more than four producers, and in Great Britain there was only one.[50] The precise extent of capital investment required is difficult to measure, but the records of machinery developed by Hyatt and others for various stages of processing give a good idea of what was involved.

A large number of devices were designed or adapted for roles in celluloid manufacture in the half-century after Hyatt's invention. Indeed, the constant changing and improving of the tools of celluloid production throughout the period was a reflection of the technical vigor that sustained the industry. The chemistry of celluloid changed little throughout its history, but the mechanical base of its manufacture was dynamic, for on it rested the final determinations of quality and economy. The technical literature treats the development of this technology adequately, but it would be useful to delineate its outlines here, if only to fully appreciate what was actually involved in establishing a novel industry.[51]

The celluloid makers borrowed from numerous technologies in devising machinery for their own. A good example was the paper industry, already highly mechanized by the late nineteenth century. In the mid-1880s Hyatt adopted complex cylinder paper-making machinery for the production of pyroxylin paper (paproxyl). Because the quality of the finished plastic depended greatly on the thoroughness and uniformity with which the pyroxylin was exposed to and mixed with the solvents, it was found useful to turn the nitrocellulose into paper just as might be done with ordinary cellulose. The cylinder machine, shown in Figure 1.1, was modified so as to apply a carefully controlled amount of camphor-alcohol solution to the paper as it came off the drying rolls into the collecting box. This yielded a modified pyroxylin that was already well saturated with camphor, simplifying and speeding the subsequent conversion operations.

Other mechanisms were used for simpler mixing processes, such as those calling for separate applications of solvent and camphor to the

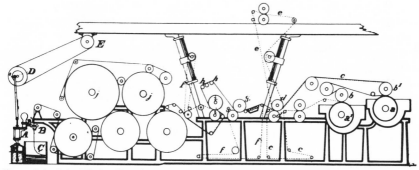

Figure 1.1. John Wesley Hyatt's patents for machinery and processes for making pyroxylin paper include this adaptation of standard paper-making and finishing machinery. (Patent number 331,713, patented December 1, 1885.)

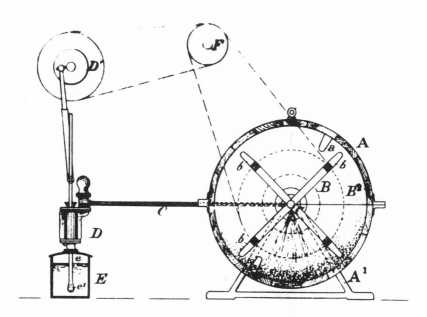

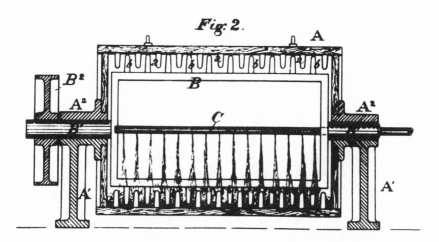

Figure 1.2. Hyatt and his co-workers devoted considerable effort to devising machinery for mixing pyroxylin with camphor and other solvents. This is from one of several patents taken out for such devices. (Patent number 326,119, patented September 15, 1885.)

pyroxylin. Another device of Hyatt was that shown in Figure 1.2, from U.S. Patent 326,119 (1885). Here, the pyroxylin, which had been thoroughly ground to a pulp and dried, was put into a drum and sprayed with the proper amount of solvent as it was well agitated. Another Hyatt machine (U.S.P. 331,241 of 1885) had an even simpler mechanism, consisting of a barrel rotating around a fixed shaft and equipped with teeth that meshed with other teeth on the shaft to effect thorough mixing, the solvent being added in bulk to the pyroxylin before mixing began. The development of a variety of machines for speedier and more complete mixing of the ingredients of celluloid was important in allowing increased production to meet market demands.

The celluloid makers borrowed from still another industry in designing machines for the final mixing of pyroxylin and camphor. The masticating machine that Hyatt adapted for this conversion step was copied from rubber manufacturing, where the mastication of raw rubber was a crucial part of production. The existence of useful devices in other industries and the ingenuity with which men like Hyatt adapted them to celluloid was a factor in the relative ease with which the American celluloid makers were able to put their enterprise on an industrial footing. Hyatt's own familiarity with mechanisms (as well as an innate mechanical talent that he applied throughout his life) was an important advantage over the earlier English pioneers.

Just as important to the eventual success of celluloid as mechanized production was mechanized fabrication of forms and final products. One of the Hyatt brothers' early patents (U.S.P. 133,229 of 1872) was for a stuffing machine designed to produce rods and tubes from celluloid (see Fig. 1.3). This machine, and modifications of it, was a mainstay of the industry, for tubes provided the initial form for a wide variety of products, including dolls, handles, vases, and other hollow articles. The Hyatt machine, like many celluloid-forming devices, operated through the application of pressure in a chamber very carefully heated by hot liquids. The fact that celluloid softened at temperatures close to 100° C was taken advantage of in many shaping machines, and was generally an attractive property to fabricators. It, for example, allowed easy production of complex decorative reliefs on such goods as mirrors, brushes, and boxes. The success of any plastic—or, indeed, of any new material—is dependent not only on the material's physical and chemical properties, but also on the integration of an appropriate mechanical base for production and handling. As with most technologies, the development of a new material requires the creation of a system of technical components. The records of the U.S. Patent Office show that the Hyatts and their colleagues did not shirk from the challenges of building the technical support system for

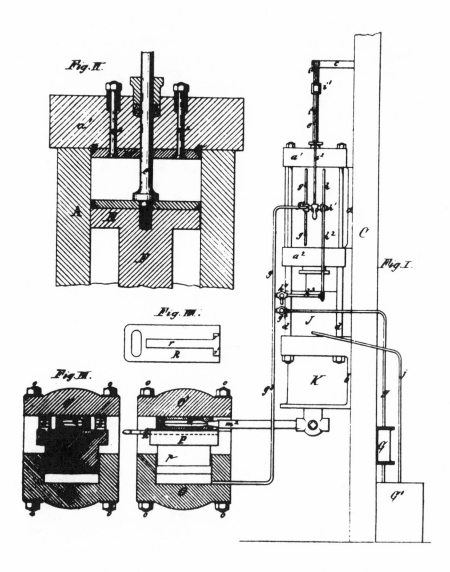

Figure 1.3. One of the earliest manufacturing machines patented by the Hyatts was this device for combining pyroxylin and camphor under pressure. (Patent number 133,229, patented November 19, 1872.)

celluloid. Between 1869 and 1891, no fewer than 64 U.S. patents relative to celluloid were issued to the Hyatt brothers alone, and they were never without friends and rivals making their own efforts.[52]

Celluloid itself, however, did not change very much after Hyatt and his colleagues set up their company. The material was tough, uniform, and resilient. It possessed a high tensile strength and was resistant to water, oils, and dilute acids. Celluloid was fairly light, having a specific gravity of about 1.4. It took a high luster and colors and coloring effects very well. It could be readily worked, and at room temperature could be sawed, drilled, turned, planed, buffed, and polished. Celluloid could be molded at a temperature just below that of boiling water. At higher heats (above 185° C), however, it would start to decompose, and it was, of course, highly flammable. Still, the combination of attractive properties in terms of working, appearance, and durability, and the cheapness and ready availability of its raw materials, made celluloid a challenge as much to imagination as to enterprise.

2

Celluloid in Its Material Context

STATED MOST simply, a material is plastic if at some time between its initial composition and its final state, it passes through a stage in which it can be molded. This definition, unfortunately, includes almost every manufactured solid. Hence, it is common, when speaking of "plastics," to exclude metals, ceramics, glasses, and woods. Because they are used largely in their unaltered natural form, it would be wise also to exclude from consideration such materials as bone, horn, ivory, and shell, while still recognizing that, in their manner of being worked, at least, these materials deserve some recognition for their kinship to modern plastics. This leaves still a group of materials that is logically divided into two not always distinct categories. One consists of those plastic materials made from compositions of naturally occurring substances, with relatively minor transformations from their natural chemical state—what may be referred to as the "natural plastics": rubber, gutta percha, shellac, and so forth. The other is made of materials that are "artificial," that is, exist only through the benefit of a major chemical transformation from the state in which they are found in nature. Celluloid was the first of this latter category. In order to understand how celluloid was perceived, however, it is necessary to give some attention to the status in the mid-nineteenth century of that first group, the natural plastics.

The Natural Plastics

While the interesting properties of the sap of trees of the species *hevea* had been known to certain peoples for many centuries and by Europeans since the voyages of Columbus, the possibilities of india rubber did not begin to be fully realized until the nineteenth century. Many Europeans were experimenting with rubber in the first decades of the century, but the credit for developing processes which allowed commercial exploitation of rubber usually goes to three Britishers working in the early 1820s. The Scottish surgeon James Syme is credited with developing the first useful solvents for rubber. Thomas Hancock's first important contribution to rubber technology was his invention of a masticator which allowed him to produce quantities of tractable rubber. And in 1823 Charles Macintosh was awarded a patent (B.P. 4,804 of 1823) for his waterproof cloth made by spreading rubber between two layers of fabric. Despite these improvements, the inability of rubber to withstand any but the smallest variations in temperature stood in the way of widespread use of the material.[1]

The secret of transforming rubber into a durable and versatile substance was discovered by Charles Goodyear in 1839 (U.S.P. 3,633, granted in 1844). This process of "vulcanization" consisted of combining raw rubber with quantities of sulfur (or sulfur compounds) under heat. Not only did this transform the rubber into a material that kept its shape and its elastic properties over a wide range of temperatures, but it also allowed the manufacture of a wide range of "rubbers"—from a highly elastic material that could be used where stretch or flexibility was most important to a very hard rubber useful when durability and hardness were objectives.

Hard rubber, also known as "vulcanite" or "ebonite," became a very popular material and the most important of the natural plastics. The first description of a process for making hard rubber was in a patent issued to Thomas Hancock in 1843 (B.P. 9,952). Hancock's 1846 patent for making molds of hard rubber (B.P. 11,135) described the first application of the material. Hard rubber was produced by increasing the sulfur used in vulcanization until it composed almost a third of the finished product. As the name "ebonite" implied, the hard rubber was a very dark material, usually colored black to give it a more uniform appearance, and this constituted one of the primary drawbacks to its use in fancy, high-cost goods.

Goodyear used the London Exhibition of 1851 to publicize the possibilities of hard rubber, displaying at his stand in the Crystal Palace such articles as combs, buttons, musical instruments, canes, and knife handles made of hard rubber. At Paris in 1855, Goodyear added to this array examples of jewelry and portraits painted on hard-rubber surfaces, as well as electric wires insulated with hard rubber. In the year 1855 Goodyear's son also patented the use of hard rubber for dental plates. In his *Gum-elastic and its Varieties, with a Detailed Account of its Applications and Uses, and of the Discovery of Vulcanization* (1855), the elder Goodyear referred to over a hundred different articles made from what he called "caoutchouc whalebone" or "caoutchouc ivory." These included toys and sporting goods, optical and surgical instruments, and items ranging in size from thimbles to boats.[2]

Thomas Hancock, in his *Personal Narrative of the Origin and Progress of the Caoutchouc or India Rubber Manufacture in England* (1857), was less concerned with hard rubber than Goodyear, but he did talk about its usefulness in making molded objects. Of special interest is Hancock's reference to the demand for hard rubber on the part of comb makers, who used the stuff by the ton, he said, preferring it over horn or tortoiseshell because it could be prepared in a less wasteful manner than more traditional materials. As we shall see later, the comb industry was similarly attracted to celluloid, and this industry's adoption of the new plastic was of singular importance. Other uses of hard rubber included telegraphic equipment, for which it was used extensively by the 1860s, and the fountain pen, which L. E. Waterman patented in 1884.[3] Of the natural plastics that were developed in the nineteenth century, none was more successful than hard rubber and none had a longer period of significant use.

A close relative of rubber, in both source and chemistry, was gutta percha. The gum of another species of tree, gutta percha differs chemically from rubber by containing oxygen. This imparts to the material some important differences in properties, the most significant of which is the inability to be vulcanized. Initially, the similarity between gutta percha and rubber attracted more attention than the differences, with less than happy results, as was pointed out by a turn-of-the-century observer:

> As a new product, it was employed for all the purposes first reserved for rubber. People became infatuated with the new substance. Patents multiplied, one in emulation with [*sic*] another. Corks, cements, threads, slippers, surgical instruments, garments, pipes, sheathing for ships, were all made of it, and even ships were made wholly of gutta percha; and it is only necessary to read the reports of the regretted M. Ballard on the London Exhibition of 1851, to be convinced of the exaggerated enthusiasm incited by this new discovery.
>
> Of all these applications—more or less judicious—there now remains but the memory.[4]

The value of gutta percha lay in the very quality that made its vulcanization impossible: just as the material was resistant to the action of sulfur, it resisted the action of almost every other corrosive or caustic substance, as well as electricity. Hence, gutta percha found its niche as the primary material for telegraph cable insulation, especially for undersea cables. Patents for cable insulation of gutta percha were issued to W. H. Barlow and Thomas Foster in 1847 and to E. W. Siemens in 1850, and the first successful underwater cable was the 25-mile line, sheathed in gutta percha, laid across the English Channel from Dover to Calais in 1850. From that point, gutta percha was the most important cable insulation until the development of synthetic resins in the 1920s and 1930s. The inert nature of the material also lent itself to uses for chemical and photographic vessels and surgical instruments.[5] These remained the important sources of demand for gutta percha, despite long continuation of the efforts to use the substance, alone or in combination with various fillers, as a general plastic.

The other natural plastics that were in vogue in the nineteenth century were composite materials—mixtures of raw materials that underwent no chemical combination in processing, but were capable of being shaped, molded, and hardened. The first of these was papier-mâché, developed in France in the eighteenth century and used for a variety of delicate articles. Consisting largely of pulped paper combined with glue and paste, papier-mâché had only limited uses. In the eighteenth century it was formed into trays, boxes, and similar small articles, often finished in imitation of lacquered wood. Papier-mâché found use in the nineteenth century as a substitute for plaster in architectural uses, such as moldings on roofs and walls and, especially, in interior room ornamentation. While being used as a plastic in some applications, papier-mâché is perhaps most appropriately thought of as an alternative to plaster or ceramics.[6]

The most important of the composition plastics were shellac-based materials. The best known of many shellac compositions was that of Samuel Peck, of New Haven, Connecticut. In the 1840s Peck was a maker of miniature cases (largely daguerreotype cases) out of the traditional leather and wood, and later from papier-mâché. It has been suggested that experience with the moldable papier-mâché may have led Peck to think of producing a more durable molding compound. In 1852 he began making his cases from a shellac and wood-fiber material. In 1854 Peck was issued U.S. Patent 11,758 for a substance "composed of gum shellac and woody fibers or other suitable fibrous material dyed to the color that may be required and ground with the shellac between hot rollers so as to be converted into a mass which when heated becomes plastic so that it can be pressed into a mold."[7] While shellac was composed of purely natural compounds, this patent clearly reflects the idea of a general-use plastic.

Alfred P. Critchlow, an English diesinker and horn-button maker who settled in Massachusetts, developed another important shellac composition. By 1853 Critchlow's shop was manufacturing a variety of molded products out of a black plastic believed to have been composed of shellac, wood resin, and lampblack. Daguerreotype cases were among his primary products. In 1858, Mark Tomlinson of Birmingham, Connecticut, took out a patent for "An Improvement in Composition for Daguerreotype Cases, Buttons and Other Uses" (U.S.P. 21,285). This was yet another shellac-based material, containing "Breckenridge or cannel-coal and ivory black" in addition to the shellac.[8] The variety of such plastics can be illustrated by some of the compositions used: a mixture of shellac, silica, and "infusorial earth" was patented as a molding material in 1868 (U.S.P. 85,018), the same year that a patent was granted for making picture frames, curtain knobs, and so forth from a composition of sawdust, rosin, and shellac (U.S.P. 73,088). To this list should be added materials made from gelatin and wood flour (U.S.P. 101,119 of 1870), and from animal products such as blood (U.S.P. 193,846 of 1877 and U.S.P. 225,638 of 1880).

The most important characteristic of these various substances was their identifiability as plastics. There was clearly a felt need for a material (or a variety of materials) that could be readily molded into useful and/or decorative forms and then depended upon to maintain its appearance. Another feature of these materials was their limited applicability. Despite some pretense to being all-purpose molding compositions, none of these natural plastics ever moved beyond narrowly defined applications, if they even achieved that. The best example of success among the shellac plastics was the phonograph record. The classic black phonograph disc was first produced early in the 1890s by Emile Berliner, but the ultimately successful record material was not Berliner's hard rubber, but rather a shellac-limestone-carbon black composition that was first utilized in 1897.[9] Shellac plastics also continued to find uses in fields where good looks were not especially important and ease of molding was—the best example being in electrical equipment, where their use long continued to rival that of hard rubber.[10]

The arrival of the natural plastics was a major episode in the emergence of new materials in the nineteenth century. They were the first significant alternatives to the traditional solid materials of manufacture and reflected a widespread desire for materials that were freed from the limitations of metal, glass, clay, and wood. The natural plastics indicated the possibilities for materials that were easily moldable and yet stable in their final manufactured form, for substances that avoided the coldness, heaviness, and chemical and electrical activity of the metals, that beckoned to artistic imagination while avoiding the fragility, cost, and weight of the glasses and ceramics, and, finally, that were in some way liberated from the stinginess of nature by combining durability and beauty in a readily available form. None of the natural plastics was able to satisfy all of these desiderata, but they clearly fostered a sense of what was really wanted.

The Ivory Problem

While the natural plastics set the stage for celluloid in one sense, their replacement was not the object of celluloid's inventors. It was not the gums and resins of trees that Parkes and Spill and Hyatt wished to replace and to surpass; it was, rather, far older and more precious materials on which they had their eye: above all, it was ivory. When Alexander Parkes was asked whether he had displayed any white parkesine at the London Exhibition of 1862, he described several objets d'art of pure white parkesine and then observed that "it was an important feature with me to make an artificial ivory."[11] As he was beginning his first commercial ventures in 1866, Parkes was issued a patent (B.P. 2,709) for making an imitation of ivory and pearl.

In the United States, John Wesley Hyatt was issued patents (U.S.P. 89,582 and others) for imitation ivory using an ivory-dust composition. Even after the invention of celluloid, he continued for several years to take out patents for imitation ivory.[12] One of the first published references to celluloid was a short notice in the *Journal of the Society of Arts* in March 1871 headed "Gun Cotton Ivory" that described the unnamed material as "a hard white substance, which, if coated with a compound of gun cotton and castor oil, resembles ivory, to which for many purposes it is superior."[13] It will be remembered that Hyatt set out on his experiments with the object of finding a replacement for ivory in billiard balls. Scepticism is sometimes voiced as to the real importance of the billiard ball in motivating Hyatt's work. While the story may seem too good to be true, there is not only the testimony of Hyatt himself (see Chap. 1, above), but also that of fellow inventor Leo Baekeland many years later:

> I may mention here, from conversations with the inventor himself, that celluloid and the celluloid industry with all that it implies, after all meant merely a big parenthesis in the life of Hyatt in his quest of a perfect billiard ball which would replace the expensive ivory article. This is so true that even during his later years, when he is well in the seventies, he has spent considerable time in the study of other plastics in his effort to still perfect billiard balls.[14]

The overstatement of the matter was Baekeland's jest, but its humor lies partially in the fact that it was based on truth. In any case, there can be little doubt that the imitating and replacing of ivory was an important goal to Hyatt.

Indeed, the finding of a substitute for ivory was a long-standing objective of nineteenth-century inventors. To get some understanding of the role of this idea in the development of celluloid and the creation of its market, it is important to realize what a popular idea it was. One reflection of the popularity of the search for an artificial ivory is the frequency with which reference to it appears in a journal like that of the Society of Arts. A particularly interesting call for an ivory substitute came in response to a Society of Arts lecture on ivory by Sir Richard Owen delivered in December 1856. A Mr. Coleman wrote after the lecture to say:

> I am far from considering the subject exhausted, and believe it would well repay the attention of any chemist who would make a series of experiments with the view of producing an artificial ivory, even if at a cost of 20s. or 40s. per lb.,* a body capable of becoming soft at a temperature 300 Fahrenheit, or forming a hard hydrate with water, would be of greater value.
>
> That our necessities will one day demand such a substance, I believe, notwithstanding the remark of Dr. Livingstone, that in Africa the supply of elephants appears almost inexhaustible, for it seems reasonable to suppose that, as civilization advances, and the demand for dentine increases, seas, rivers, and plains will become exhausted of their ivory-producing inhabitants. As the coal-field has supplied the deficiencies of the forest, and as the pump will probably someday supply the deficiencies of the coal cellar,† so doubtless artificial dentine will supply the place of natural, and a great benefactor will he be to the toothless community who first produces it.[15]

The imminent exhaustion of ivory supplies alarmed numerous observers in the latter half of the nineteenth century. A short item in the *Journal of the Society of Arts* in 1864 remarked:

> At the close of the last century England did not work more than 192,600 lb. of ivory per annum; in 1827 the demand had risen to 364,784 lb., which supposes the death of 3,040 male elephants per annum, yielding 6,080 tusks, averaging 601 lb. each. At present England consumes 1,000,000 lb. per annum, or upwards of three times the consumption of 1827; and therefore the number of elephants killed for England alone must be 8,333 or thereabouts. About 4,000 men lose their lives annually in the pursuit after ivory.[16]

An article in the *New York Times* for 7 July 1867 picked up the same theme, remarking on the certain extinction of elephants and lamenting the lack of success in the search for an ivory substitute.[17] An ivory dealer's pamphlet prepared for the 1876 Centennial Exhibition at Philadelphia estimated the annual consumption of ivory at that time to be about two

---

*Cf. the average 1854 price of ivory of about 7 shillings per pound.

†An allusion to the promise of petroleum.

million pounds and went on to admit that "there is no doubt, that the destructive war, carried on of late against elephants, tends gradually to decrease their number, and to accelerate their final extirpation."[18] Throughout the last half of the nineteenth century there was a widely perceived "ivory problem."

The frequent comments on the impending ivory shortage were matched by frequent references to new-found solutions.* The *Journal of the Society of Arts* for 1 December 1865 included a note on an artificial ivory made by a complex process involving the treatment of rubber or gutta percha dissolved in chloroform.[19] An article of the journal in 1866 referred to a substance called "Parisian marble" as an artificial ivory made from papier-mâché and gelatine.[20] A popular book of "practical receipts" in the early 1870s repeated the rubber-in-chloroform formula for making "the most successful imitation of natural ivory."[21] Hard rubber itself, as has been noted above, was touted by Goodyear as "caoutchouc ivory." The New York billiard ball makers were not the only ones concerned about the ivory supply, nor were Hyatt and the other celluloid experimenters alone in trying to find a solution to the perceived problem.

Was there really an ivory problem? Certainly the impression of one was widespread, and it was the popular impression that was most significant in motivating would-be inventors. But the true importance of that perception becomes clear only in light of the facts about the supply and consumption of ivory. There is little room in a simple model of supply and demand balance for considerations of the relationship between real needs and perceived needs in stimulating technological change. And yet here is a case where the perceptions of need were common even as, so the data suggest, the market as yet showed no shortfall. These data are not complete or conclusive, but their basic thrust is unmistakable. The ivory problem, in the nineteenth century, was largely a myth.

Even at the time, there were those who reacted against the sometimes shrill warnings about the ivory supply. One particularly strident warning in the *Journal of the Society of Arts* in June 1882[22] drew this reply in the same journal a few months later: "There has been an outcry and discussion of late as to falling supplies of ivory, and the probability of a dearth of this valuable raw material; but at present there would appear to be little foundation for this fear, whatever there may be for the future." The writer then offered the official import returns for the United Kingdom as evidence:

---

*As early as 1839 a British patent (8,131) was taken out for "compositions to resemble ivory, bone, horn, mother-of-pearl, and other substances—applicable to the manufacture of handles of knives, forks, razors and various other articles."

Year	Hundredweights
1840	5,469
1850	9,396
1860	10,854
1870	12,590
1875	16,258
1880	13,345[23]

The picture at midcentury was clearly one of rising supplies, doubtless aided by the European colonial expansion in Africa.

Later in the century, as data become more complete, there is nothing to change this picture. Obviously, demand was rising just as supplies were, but the evidence does not bear out the notion that supplies were not keeping up. Figure 2.1 summarizes the price history of ivory imported into the United States from 1875 to 1905, based on the highest-quality material

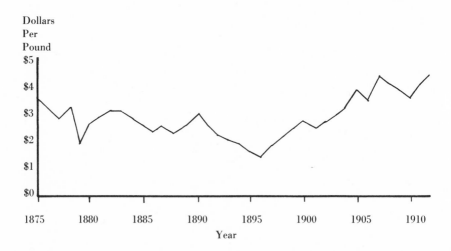

Figure 2.1. Prices per pound of the highest-quality ivory on the New York market, 1875-1912. Ivory prices did not begin to rise significantly until after 1900. From George F. Kunz, *Ivory and the Elephant* (Garden City, N.Y.: Doubleday, Page & Co., 1916), pp. 443-448.

bought at New York. Figure 2.2 depicts the pattern of ivory imports into the United States between 1884 and 1905. The combined picture of relatively steady prices and rising supplies belies any idea of scarcity in the last decades of the nineteenth century, and this picture is confirmed by data from other countries. The ivory problem existed more in the mind than in the market.

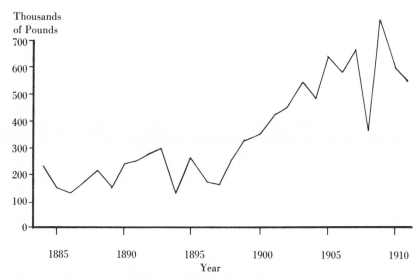

Figure 2.2. Total ivory imports into the United States, 1884-1911 (in thousands of pounds). Late-nineteenth-century data does not support the notion that ivory was increasingly scarce as the century wore on. From Kunz, *Ivory and the Elephant*, p. 448.

Yet the perception of a real or impending ivory shortage cannot be dismissed as simply an illusion. There is little question that it spurred the search for an artificial substitute, and therefore deserves a more careful appraisal. If the search for a substitute does not seem to have been based on an aggregate shortage of ivory, then might it not stem from the uses to which that ivory was put?

These uses changed little in the last half of the nineteenth century. The ivory dealer's circular referred to earlier, for the 1876 Philadelphia Exhibition, included descriptions and price lists for piano keys, billiard balls, knife handles and slabs of ivory for fans, scrolls, book covers, brush backs, and stick and umbrella handles.[24] An article on the ivory trade in the *Journal of the Society of Arts* for 25 November 1898 gave billiard balls, piano keys, comb and knife handles as the principal ivory goods, supplemented by a variety of fancy carved articles.[25] George F. Kunz, of Tiffany's in New York, listed in his 1916 treatise on ivory a large number of uses in addition to the major ones. The list of fancy goods was extensive: trays, hair-receivers, glove stretchers, cold cream boxes, tooth powder boxes, shoehorns, nail-powder boxes, hairpin stands, pin boxes, hatpin stands, glove-powder boxes, talcum powder boxes, salve boxes, jewel boxes, pomade boxes, vaseline boxes, the backs and handles of mirrors, hair brushes, hat brushes, pincushions, buttonhooks, cuticle knives, shaving mirrors, shaving brushes, military brushes, whiskbrooms, velvet brushes, nailscrapers, and combs.[26] This impressive list can be largely reduced to "boxes and handles" and reaffirms the impression that ivory, whatever may have been its intrinsic popularity, was not a very versatile material.

The Significance of Billiard Balls

To what extent was celluloid actually developed and sold as a substitute for ivory? While it is clear that the inventors of the material had an artificial ivory in mind, it remains to be seen to what degree the material that they eventually developed corresponded to such a thing. To measure such correspondence requires not only a look at the products made of celluloid, but also a somewhat more specific idea of what criteria would have to be met by an artificial ivory. Ivory is not simply bone or even teeth; it is "that modification of dentine or tooth substance which in a transverse section shows lines of different colors running in circular arcs, and forming by their decussation minute, lozenge-shaped spaces, and which is represented by every portion of any transverse section of an elephant's tusk."[27] A good imitation ivory would have to be more than a particular shade of white, but would have to be made in such a way as to show striations of a characteristic kind. The material would, furthermore, have to be very smooth and capable of taking a high polish. It would have to be fairly hard, but partially moldable at a steam heat. It would have to be carvable as well. The fact is that celluloid was indeed the first man-made material to have all of these properties.

The substitution and imitation of materials is, however, a complex affair. The experience of celluloid as a prospective material for billiard balls is a remarkable illustration of this, for despite its virtues it could not truly succeed in this role. The billiard ball was the one object for which ivory was not only preferred, but required. Handles could be made of fine woods or of metals, piano keys were sometimes capped with ebony or porcelain, and fancy goods of every sort could be made from a variety of expensive substances. But only ivory would do for billiard balls. Lest this sound trivial to the modern ear, it should be pointed out that billiards was one of the few important indoor sports in the nineteenth century, particularly among the well-to-do. A Society of Arts lecturer stated as late as 1906 that billiards constituted the primary source of demand for ivory.[28] An equally important fact was that only ivory of the highest quality was used in the making of billiard balls.[29] Only a small fraction of the tusks sold in any particular lot of ivory was suitable for balls—sometimes no more than one tusk out of a lot of fifty. The difficulties in manufacturing billiard balls were considerable. The ball had to be centered in line with the center of the tusk so that it would be properly balanced. Special care had to be taken to prevent cracking or heating in the process of cutting. Finally, the seasoning time for a finished ball ranged from eighteen months to two years.[30] The luxury of a billiard ball was not only in its material but also in its craftsmanship.

Even without a real "ivory problem," there indeed could have been a "billiard ball problem." Evidence that this was indeed so came from a New York billiards supplier writing in the 1850s:

> The ivory brought from the island of Ceylon is the best that can be used for billiard balls, the tusks being far more solid than those from Continental Asia, and more elastic in proportion to their density than any other. They are dreadfully dear, however; and if any inventive genius would discover a substitute for ivory, possessing those qualities which make it valuable to the billiard player, he would make a handsome fortune for himself, and earn our sincerest gratitude.[31]

The same supplier backed up his words with the offer of the $10,000 award that was said to have spurred the efforts of John Wesley Hyatt. Hyatt did patent a composition for making billiard balls before he discovered the formula for celluloid. In fact, he and his brother established the Albany Billiard Ball Company as one of their first commercial ventures. Yet once he turned his attention to celluloid, Hyatt did not find the material particularly useful for billiard balls. Many years later, he remarked on the considerable difficulties he encountered in trying to use celluloid for this particular purpose. His billiard ball company manufactured balls with a shellac or composition core coated with collodion or thin celluloid, but even this seems to have been less than successful, as suggested by the story he once told about the Colorado saloon keeper who wrote to say that occasionally a sharp collison of the collodion-covered balls would produce a report like that of a percussion cap, causing every man in the establishment to draw his gun.[32]

The extent to which celluloid actually was used for billiard balls is impossible to determine. The Albany Billiard Ball Company received a license in the early 1870s for manufacturing billiard and bagatelle balls from celluloid, and occasional descriptions were published in technical and popular journals of celluloid ball manufacture.[33] By the late 1890s, however, the Albany company's advertisements spoke only of "standard composition" balls, and no mention was made of celluloid.[34] As Leo Baekeland's reference to Hyatt's continued search for the perfect billiard ball implied (above, at n. 14), celluloid was never a satisfactory substitute for this most special of ivory products. Criticisms of celluloid's use for this purpose were common, many of them critical of the material's elasticity

when compared with ivory, which, after all, would always remain the
standard.[35] The ivory billiard ball was replaced only with the arrival of
Baekeland's own candidate, bakelite.

This digression on billiard balls gives some indication of the complex
factors involved in substituting a new material for an old one. There was
clearly a perceived need for a substitute for ivory in billiard balls, not so
much because of the widely touted ivory shortage—that was not a real
factor until the twentieth century—as because of the intrinsic difficulties
presented by the manufacture of balls from ivory. On the other hand, the
criteria for a successful substitute in this particular case were more difficult to meet than perhaps in any other area of manufacture. This was
because in this one field, much more than in any other, the qualities of
ivory dictated the standards involved. By definition, a billiard ball was a
ball made of ivory. Thus, despite the greater ease of manufacture and the
ready availability of the material, celluloid balls could not replace ivory
ones unless celluloid matched the older substance in such properties as
elasticity and hardness as well as in superficial appearance. This,
celluloid did not do; therefore, in this application, it was always an inferior product, to be used only where considerations of cost overrode all
others.

Dental Plates: The Competitive Challenge

Celluloid was eventually much used as an imitation ivory, but the first
commercial success of Hyatt's celluloid was not in the replacement of
ivory, but rather, of a newer and cheaper material, hard rubber. Celluloid
challenged rubber on very special and carefully chosen ground—dental
plates. The establishment of the Albany Dental Plate Company in 1870,
described in Chapter 1, marked the beginning of the first two years of
Hyatt's celluloid manufacture, years devoted almost exclusively to producing dental plates. Just how Hyatt came to shift his attention from
billiard balls to dental plates is not clear, but the possibilities of the dental
plate market must not have been difficult to discern. This time, however,
the opportunities were presented, not by the difficulties of working with
the older substance nor by its real or impending scarcity, but by man-
made monopoly. The holders of the Goodyear Company's patent on the
use of hard rubber for dental plates charged a royalty to every dispenser
of hard-rubber plates, a charge apparently found irksome, if not onerous,
by dentists everywhere.[36]

Appearing in several numbers of the *Dental Cosmos* (a journal spon-
sred by a dental supply house) in the first half of 1871 was this notice from
the Albany Dental Plate Company:

We take great pleasure in announcing to the Dental Profession, that we are in possession of a newly-invented and patented material for Dental Plates or bases for artificial teeth, that cannot fail to delight every dentist who desires a better material for the purpose than hard rubber.

This base consists of a new and peculiar composition of solid collodion, which possesses all the advantages that have ever been hoped from collodion or pyroxyline, while it is entirely free from the difficulties heretofore experienced in manipulating that substance, as well as from liability to shrink and change form after being made into artificial plates.[37]

This was the first announcement of a celluloid product. The allusions to past failures suggests a context of expectations and frustrations surrounding the application of pyroxylin for molded products, a context that is not obvious from most of the discussions surrounding celluloid's invention. By comparing their product to previous efforts, the Hyatts also suggested that the notion of applying celluloid to dental plates did not come to them as an original idea, but was instead derived from knowledge of others' experiences. The advertisement went on to list the advantages of celluloid plates: lighter and stronger than hard rubber, truer in color, free from unpleasant taste, acid resistant, harmless in the mouth (lacking the mercury that was used in coloring rubber plates), more easily and quickly fitted, and more comfortable to wear than rubber plates. The blank plates were offered for $1.00 apiece, and the complete apparatus for molding the plates was priced at $7.00. Price was not one of the touted advantages of celluloid. Contemporary advertisements for rubber gave the price of dental rubber at about $2.50 per pound. A typical hard-rubber dental plate weighed no more than half an ounce and thus contained no more than about 8¢ worth of rubber.* To be sure, royalties would have to be added to the costs of using rubber, but even so, it is clear that celluloid was being offered as a luxury alternative.

Unfortunately for the Hyatts, technical difficulties made their product a less than satisfactory alternative. Shortly after the appearance of the advertisement quoted above, there appeared another item in the *Dental Cosmos* from the Albany Dental Plate Company, this one reflecting considerable concern over the fate of their enterprise. In the form of a letter from Isaiah Smith Hyatt, it began:

I have received numerous letters from members of the Dental profession who are using the 'Celluloid Base,' and who, while speaking of their successes, also give instances of failure or of imperfections existing in some of

---

*A nineteenth-century hard-rubber plate without teeth from the collections of the Division of Medical Sciences, National Museum of American History, Smithsonian Institution, was weighed to determine this.

the plates which they have used. It is impracticable to answer these letters individually, and hence I desire to do so collectively through the *Dental Cosmos*. Similar but unexpressed queries in the minds of others may be met by the same means.

The difficulties referred to may be summarized about as follows:

1. Some of the plates have had a strong camphoric or pungent gummy taste.
2. Some have become soft in the mouth, or sufficiently so for the teeth to loosen.
3. Plates have warped after having been adjusted in patients' mouths.
4. Plates have been found that were flaky or laminar.

'What is the matter?' dentists ask. 'We had great hopes of the new base, but if it works this way, we shall, in great disappointment, be obliged to go back to rubber.'[38]

Hyatt went on to explain that these difficulties had been encountered by only a few dentists and that they were the unavoidable symptoms of a new manufacture. They were said to have been corrected by variations in the composition of the plates and by greater care in their manufacture. This advertisement was probably the first using the term *celluloid*; all subsequent notices used the new name freely.

As late as 1873, further advertisements of the Albany Dental Plate Company appeared in the pages of the *Dental Cosmos*, these of a more positive nature: "The dental profession may now feel assured that we are producing Celluloid plates of uniform character, possessing the required qualities of strength, permanency of form, beauty of color, and freedom from taste, smell, or any other objectionable feature."[39] Many testimonials were added to this advertisement. Notices of the product also appeared in England, with extensive testimonials appended.[40] An advertisement in the *Dental Cosmos* later in 1873 emphasized that the use of celluloid plates was completely free of any restrictions arising from the Goodyear patent on "vulcanite" plates. It also announced lower prices— 60¢ a plate, down from $1.00.[41] This last advertisement appeared in the name of the Celluloid Manufacturing Company, out of Newark, reflecting the fact that dental plate manufacture did not cease with the creation of the new, more broadly based company.[42]

Despite the fact that celluloid dental plates continued to be produced at least until after the end of the century,[43] they never replaced hard rubber as the most important material for plates. Some of the reasons for this were technical. One observer spoke of the abandonment of celluloid in favor of hard rubber "on account of the pronounced taste of camphor in the dental plates, of the apprehension of practitioners over the inflammability of the product and of its warping under the influence of heat."[44] Celluloid never escaped the problems that plagued it from the very beginning of its use as a denture material. Another reason that celluloid was not able to compete successfully with hard rubber was that its price always made it the more expensive substance, especially after Goodyear's patent control over dental rubber ended. Its one major advantage was in its color. Hard rubber was naturally opaque brown, and making plates from it that had any kind of acceptable gumlike color required the use of large amounts of materials like zinc white and vermilion,[45] this last material being a mercury compound whose presence in the mouth was often a cause of concern. Celluloid, on the other hand, could be colored the proper shade of red with much smaller amounts of vermilion or even with harmless organic dyes, and was hence considered a healthier material. Simply being prettier and healthier, however, did not make celluloid a success in dentistry.

Substitution and Substance

As a material for billiard balls and dental plates, celluloid was not a total failure. To a limited degree, celluloid continued to be applied to both uses until other plastics (phenolics in the case of billiard balls and acrylics for dentures) replaced both it and all other competitors in the twentieth century. There was an extent to which celluloid worked satisfactorily in both of these specialized uses. On the other hand, the new material was not a success either. In the case of billiard balls, celluloid was always an inferior material, and the search for ivory substitutes continued throughout the remainder of the nineteenth century. Celluloid was always a secondary material for dental plates, used only when particular qualities such as appearance were of paramount importance and a premium price was no deterrent. Celluloid did not and could not achieve any status as an important material through these uses.

Celluloid's problems in these applications suggest some of the basic issues confronting a new material. The substitution of a new material for an older one in any particular application involves two basic sets of considerations: technical and economic. The problems of the celluloid billiard ball illustrate the complexity of the technical dimensions, just as those of celluloid dental plates characterize the economic. Any material traditionally put to a particular use possesses a number of physical qualities that suit it to that use. Some of these are more critical than others, and it is necessary for the promoters of a substitute material to differentiate these in evaluating the chances for success. Celluloid could certainly be made to look like an ivory billiard ball, but it could never behave like the real article, and in this case properties such as density and elasticity were more important than appearance. Thus, despite celluloid's economic advantages, its technical limitations were too great. Only with the appearance of a material that could be produced with a wide range of physical characteristics, such as the phenolic resins, could a substitute for ivory in such a use be satisfactory. Despite its versatility in appearance, its chemistry defined celluloid's physical properties within narrow, inflexible limits.

The effort to make celluloid a popular substitute for hard rubber in dentures ran up against different problems. The pressures for substitution were mild and temporary, created not by natural shortages but by short-term patent restrictions and monopoly control over raw material supply. Once such restrictions were ended (through expiration or ineffectiveness of patents) and the number of independent rubber suppliers began growing, the pressures for substitution of rubber in dentistry subsided. Celluloid could then compete only on the basis of its properties, which, as has been seen, were as often prejudicial against its use as they may have been favorable.

When pressures for substitution were minor or temporary, the commercial success of the new material required clearly superior properties at a competitive price or, alternately, equivalent properties combined with significant economies. The fact that celluloid lacked either of these combinations did not prevent its entry into the denture market, but it kept the new material from becoming anything but a secondary, specialty substance. For celluloid to find important markets it would have to replace something well that sorely needed replacing, drive a competitive material from its outlets by dint of its own properties or price, or create new markets where they had not before existed. In finding a secure niche for celluloid, its promoters eventually took all of these paths.

3

The Search for Markets

WITHOUT A true necessity to acknowledge its parentage, celluloid was a sort of technological bastard, whose first struggles for respectability and a place in the market were difficult ones. The problems it encountered were remarkable evidence of the complexity of introducing a new material into a society and an economic environment where such a thing was uncommon. The evolution from inventors' fancies to entrepreneurs' challenges to manufacturers' commodities mirrors an evolution of attitudes that, in some ways, continues up to this day. The history of this evolution is also an episode in the constant struggle between images and economic and technical realities that surrounds the creation and adoption of any important technology.

The Problems of Parkesine

Alexander Parkes was the first person to apply himself conscientiously to producing a pyroxylin plastic. Because his invention was the first to be the subject of attempts at large-scale production and marketing, the motives for his long years of work are of particular interest. Thanks to the wide-ranging nature of the testimony that Parkes gave in the Spill–Celluloid Manufacturing Company litigation of the late 1870s, as well as the existence of other sources, such as patents, articles, and pamphlets, Parkes's thoughts about his work are perhaps better known than those of any who followed him. What Parkes said as well as what he did reveals a great deal about both the mentality and the economics behind the emergence of the first artificial plastic.

While Parkes's background and professional interests prepared him for working with a wide variety of materials, as we saw in Chapter 1, it is nonetheless startling to discover how long the idea of a pyroxylin plastic preoccupied him. His 1878 testimony suggested that his interest in making a plastic from pyroxylin had begun as early as 1851,[1] the year that Ar-

41

cher's wet plate (collodion) photographic process was introduced. Parkes described in vivid terms how his attention was drawn to the subject:

> Q: . . . what induced you to turn your attention to the manufacture of the substance which you subsequently called 'Parkesine'[?]
> A: From the knowledge I had of the importance of that substance in its various applications to the arts from the valuable properties I had observed when thin solutions of collodion were allowed to become solids by evaporation. . . .
> Q: At the time when your attention was first directed to the preparation of substances such as Parkesine had you seen any specimen of such substance[?]
> A: Never.
> Q: Then what do you mean by your knowledge of the application of these substances to the arts—
> A: What I mean—it was only known as a photographic agent at that time and always used in a state of thin solution and I determined then to manufacture solid articles principally composed of nitro cellulose and manufacture [them] at the lowest possible cost.[2]

The idea of a plastic from nitrocellulose came from the combination of Parkes's interest in novel substances and his observation of the general usefulness of nitrocellulose in other forms.

Parkes's first patent revealed even more directly the sense of the latent possibilities of "guncotton" that motivated his early work. The provisional specification for British Patent 2,359 of 1855 reads as follows:

> My improvements consist in the treatment of oils by the action of chloride of sulphur, alone or with other substances, so as to produce an elastic, solid or adhesive compound; and in the use of gun cotton or other similar compounds in pyroxylic spirit (wood naphtha), or other solvents of such compounds, alone or compounded with gums, resins, or other substances. The above preparations and solutions I use for waterproofing and manufacturing various articles having properties analogous to those made from india-rubber or gutta-percha.

In the patent itself, Parkes went on to say,

> It is well known that a solution of gun cotton has been used principally as a photographic agent and in surgical operations but my object is to employ collodion or its compounds for manufacturing purposes generally.

The patent was primarily a description of possible uses for collodion or a collodion-based compound. These included using a solution as a waterproof coating to be applied to silks and other fabrics or to threads, yarns, leather, plaster, or wood; decorating fabrics or paper with a coating of the material; making sheets, either singly or compounded, transparent or colored, that would be useful for book-binding, button manufacture, "and other applications where a hard, strong, brilliant material is required"; and making compounds that could be molded or used as ornamentation. The patent also mentioned substances that could be added to the plastic compounds to reduce the flammability that was, even at that early date, recognized as being a problem with any nitrocellulose plastic.

Later patents issued to Parkes showed little change in his concept of the functions and purposes of his invention. British Patent 2,675 of 1864 described unpromising compounds of guncotton and other substances to be used "for waterproofing, for coating, for making sheets, tubes, or other forms, and for insulating telegraph wires." Parkes's patent 2,709 of 1866 was issued largely for methods used in forming parkesine into imitations of ivory and pearl—the method suggested for accomplishing the former being very similar to that adopted later for celluloid. In patent 1,695 of 1867 Parkes described the use of parkesine for "improvements in ornamenting surfaces of paper, woven fabric and other material, to render them suitable for bookbinding and other similar uses." The following year Parkes was granted a patent (B.P. 1,614 of 1868) for "Improvements in the Manufacture of Parkesine or Compounds of Pyroxylin, to render such materials more suitable for making Billiard Balls, and for other purposes." Taken together, these patents reflected several consistent themes in Parkes's own appraisal of his new material. One of these was the ornamental potential of parkesine; another, its waterproofing possibilities; yet a third, its possible use for insulating telegraph lines. The evolution of these themes into marketing strategies is suggestive of the difficulties facing the nineteenth-century inventor-entrepreneur, especially one having a product with less-than-obvious uses.

The emergence of parkesine from the imagination and laboratory of Alexander Parkes was marked by a single well-known and well-described event, the London Exhibition of 1862. The *Illustrated Catalogue* of the exhibition included, among hundreds of undistinctive entries, one entry under the heading of Class IV, Eastern Annexe, East Side 1112, "PARKES, ALEXANDER, *Birmingham.* —Patent Parkesine of various colors; hard elastic, transparent, opaque, and waterproof."[3] Class IV was for "Animal and Vegetable Substances used in Manufactures," and Parkes's exhibit was put in Section C, "Vegetable Substances used in Manufactures, &c," along with such other curiosities as imitation horsehair, trout and salmon flies, baskets, canes, and india-rubber goods.[4] It is significant that parkesine appeared in this class and not in, say, Class II, "Chemical Substances and Products, and Pharmaceutical Processes." Despite the chemical transformations involved in making parkesine, it was easier to think of the plastic as a modified natural material than as a truly new or "synthetic" substance. This is one of the reasons that parkesine and the other pyroxylin plastics seemed less novel to persons in the nineteenth century than they do, in hindsight, to us.

It was not uncommon for an exhibitor at such an event as the London International Exhibition to prepare a leaflet or handbill to serve as an advertisement of his booth and an information sheet for visitors to take home with them. Alexander Parkes prepared such an advertisement, and because it was the first public announcement of the existence and virtues of an artificial plastic, it is worth repeating here in its entirety.

PARKESINE

A new material and manufacture now exhibited for the first time, has from its valuable properties induced the Inventor to Patent the discovery in England and France, and to devote his attention for the last ten years to the development of the capabilities and application of this beautiful substance to the Arts.

In the Case are shown a few illustrations of the numerous purposes for which it may be applied, such as *Medallions, Salvers, Hollow Ware, Tubes, Buttons, Combs, Knife Handles, Pierced and Fret Work, Inlaid Work, Bookbinding, Card Cases, Boxes, Pens, Penholders, &c.,* —these have been produced solely by the exhibitor (as Samples), not having yet arranged a systematic manufacture for the material. It can be made *Hard as Ivory, Transparent* or *Opaque,* of any degree of *Flexibility,* and is also *Waterproof;* may be of the most *Brilliant Colours,* can be used in the *Solid, Plastic* or *Fluid State,* may be worked in *Dies* and *Pressure,* as *Metals,* may be *Cast* or used as a *Coating* to a great variety of substances; can be spread or worked in a similar manner to *India Rubber,* and has stood exposure to the atmosphere for years without change or decomposition. And by the system of ornamentation Patented by Henry Parkes in 1861, the most perfect imitation of *Tortoise-shell, Woods,* and an endless variety of effects can be produced. Specimens of which may be seen in the Case.

> Patentee and Exhibitor,
> ALEX. PARKES,
> Birmingham[5]

The emphasis on versatility was more a symptom of uncertainty than a boast of accomplishment.

Parkes tried to show that anything could be made of the material and that nothing in particular really was. In his patent suit testimony, Parkes listed many of the objects he displayed: "Combs, brush-backs, bookcovers, knife handles, telegraph wire covered with parkesine, textile fabrics coated with parkesine—sheets in various colors in imitation of malachite—tortoiseshell and many other figures—medallions—part of a set of teeth set in nitrocellulose—carvings and others."[6] This jumbled picture of Parkes's wares was reinforced by the testimony of his son, Henry, who added to his father's list small carved heads, tubes of lace coated with transparent parkesine, buttons in a wide variety of colors, threads coated in the same variety of colors, parkesine inlaid with gold, silver, and pearl for a brooch, a medallion of Pope Pius IX, semitransparent crosses, a brooch which featured Cupid on a swan, and a small carved head of Christ, among other items.[7] Henry Parkes's list emphasized more than his father's the significance of artistry and color in the presentation of parkesine. Parkesine was seen as a potentially important material for the artist. To Parkes moldability and color were two of the most essential characteristics of the material.

Those who reported on the 1862 display of parkesine remarked above all on the versatility of the substance. A report that appeared in two different guides to the exhibition read:

> Among the most extraordinary substances shown is a new material called 'Parkesine,' from the name of its discoverer, the product of chloroform and castor oil, which produces a substance as hard as horn but as flexible as leather, capable of being cast or stamped, painted, dyed, or carved, and which, above all, can be produced, in any quantity, at a lower price than gutta percha.[8]

The commentator was simply wrong about parkesine's composition, of course, but he was as vague as everyone else about just what it was good for.

When an East London waterproofer and india-rubber manufacturer, George Spill, and his brother Daniel decided to try to convert Parkes's invention into something more than a laboratory curiosity, it became necessary to move beyond vague generalities about the versatility of the material and to develop ideas about promising markets. The first indication of this necessity came in a prospectus issued to attract buyers of shares in the newly incorporated Parkesine Company, Limited, in mid-1866. The purpose of the company was described as being

> to acquire the exclusive right of using the Patent Inventions of Mr. Alexander Parkes, in the production of the new substance known as Parkesine, and carrying on the manufacture thereof, and also to acquire the exclusive right to use his Patent Invention for the manufacture of Electric Conductors, which, when coated with Parkesine it is expected will be of sufficent strength and endurance for all purposes of Deep Sea Telegraphy, without any further protection or covering.[9]

The wide possibilities for parkesine were described further in the prospectus, but the emphasis was clearly on telegraphy:

> Parkesine remains unaffected by the heat of tropical climates, and is not subject to become brittle by cold, nor impaired by oxidation.

It may be made opaque or transparent, hard or flexible, and of any colour. In its hard form, it can be applied for carding, roving and spinning rollers, or bosses for cotton, linen, silk and woollen machinery, insulators for telegraph poles, telegraphic and philosophical instruments, bookbinding, picture frames, panelling for carriages, and works of art.

In its flexible condition it may be extensively used for insulating telegraphic wire, for the manufacture of tubing, for coating textile fabrics, and fuses for blasting purposes, &c.; and, in its fluid state, as varnishes and paint for general purposes, and more especially for coating iron ships.

The practicability of shallow and deep sea telegraphy having been conclusively and successfully demonstrated, the demand for insulating materials has of late years greatly increased, and must now necessarily be very great; and, the supply of ordinary insulating materials becoming precarious, the Company is justified in anticipating that an extensive and profitable trade will arise from the application of Parkesine to this purpose.[10]

The only difficulty with the company's "anticipation" was that parkesine simply was not a good material for telegraph insulation: it shrank too much. Besides, it was, then and in the later form of xylonite and celluloid, never cheaper than gutta percha. It must be remembered, however, that 1866 saw the first success at laying a permanent Atlantic cable and that both Britain and America were ecstatic over the achievement. Small wonder that a small group of entrepreneurs with an unknown product should wish to link Cyrus Field's success with their own purposes.[11]

The most important new feature in the 1866 prospectus was not the use of parkesine as cable insulation, but rather the entire change in tone. With the exception of a brief reference to "works of art," the idea of parkesine as a beautiful material for making fine things was absent. Parkes, in 1862, by both his advertisement and his display, was at pains to show his invention as a new tool of the artist. The appeal to financiers and industrialists four years later, however, was in terms of the excessively mundane—spinning rollers and fuse coatings. This change in perspective was not the doing of Alexander Parkes, as he himself testified years afterwards:

When I was manufacturing Parkesine myself my principal object was to make works of art and things of high class value but when I negotiated this thing on a large scale everybody connected with the movement from the commencement of Messieurs Spill and Company onward urged the necessity of making Parkesine as cheaply as possible—it was to be dealt in in tons instead of pounds.[12]

On the other hand, Parkes probably did not vigorously resist this shift in attitude. His presentation before the Society of Arts in 1865, for example, contained several references to the cheapening of his invention, including a rash assertion that parkesine could be produced in large quantities for as little as one shilling a pound.[13]

The failure of parkesine as a coating for telegraph lines was mercifully quick. Once the Parkesine Company established manufacture of the material about the beginning of the year 1867, nothing was heard of the production of telegraph insulation, although experiments continued. This direction having proved fruitless, the presentation of parkesine reverted to images of a wonderfully versatile and attractive substance good for almost everything but for nothing in particular. When a display of parkesine was being prepared for the Paris Universal Exhibition of 1867, Parkes drew up a six-page pamphlet to accompany the exhibit. This pamphlet was considerably more detailed than the leaflet distributed at London five years before, describing the full range of Parkes's work on parkesine as well as some technical details about how the material was manufactured. The careful descriptions of the production of parkesine contrasted with the confusion about the substance that was reflected in the 1862 descriptions of parkesine as a "product of chloroform and castor oil." The adoption of the new material would be furthered more, so the thinking went now, by a wider understanding of what it was, rather than by efforts to keep its composition secret.

Yet the 1867 statement continued to be vague about the purposes and functions of parkesine. At its beginning, Parkes offered this explanation for his efforts: "For years previous to 1850 I was strongly impressed with the importance and want of a substance to take the place of certain natural productions, such as ivory, tortoiseshell, india rubber, gutta percha, &c., &c., and in the year 1850 I directed my attention to the peculiar properties of Pyroxyline and similar substances."[14] Not only were ivory and gutta percha tossed together, but they were supplemented by "&c., &c.," another suggestion of that curious combination of "anything" and "nothing in particular."

The Parkesine Company failed, and by the end of 1868 its assets were being liquidated. The liquidation advertisement listed the sorts of products it had tried to sell: knife handles, brooches, earrings, chains, envelope and writing cases, inkstands, pads, and many unmanufactured sheets.[15] There were numerous opinions as to why the company had failed. Alexander Parkes blamed the management of the enterprise;[16] Daniel Spill said that it was a technical failure, that "they couldn't make the goods pure enough and white enough to suit the market";[17] and his nephew, who was a foreman in the works, suggested that the plant had never been able to produce saleable articles.[18] Most of the evidence indicates that the failure of parkesine was due to the manufacturers' inability to reconcile two conditions for success: consistently satisfactory quality and low price.

The roots of this failure lay deeper than that, however. While the inability to combine quality with low price may be considered a largely technical deficiency, due to the composition of parkesine and ignorance of the importance of camphor, it was also due to some fundamental problems in conceptualizing the material. As long as Alexander Parkes was concerned with making an attractive plastic material that lent itself to enhancing the skills of an artist or craftsman, he could produce a substance which was at once aesthetically attractive and workable. Once the notion of making a cheap substitute for everything became dominant, however, cheap and impure raw materials began to be substituted for higher grades, shortcuts in processing replaced careful laboratory procedures, and insufficient seasoning and testing caused faulty articles to be sent out to market. Of course, the shift from the experimental to the production stage in any technology engenders tendencies toward cheaper and quicker processes, but the feeling that parkesine had to be made cheap enough to substitute for products like rubber and gutta percha as well as for ivory or tortoiseshell allowed the push for cheapness to overwhelm all other considerations. Furthermore, the effort to market parkesine in a wide variety of forms and objects dissipated the impact on the market and on the public that a more straightforward substitution of one material for another would have had.

The Xylonite Episode

In May 1869, Daniel Spill, with a number of financial backers, established the Xylonite Company at the works of the defunct Parkesine Company.[19] This institution was to resurrect the production of parkesine, only now under the name of xylonite. The production methods of the Xylonite Company differed little from those of its predecessor, and its products were largely the same as well. A circular of the Xylonite Company dated 31 March 1871 offered this description of the material:

> XYLONITE: a substitute for Ivory, Bone, Horn, Tortoiseshell, Hard Woods, Vulcanite, Papier Mache, Marbles, Brass, and Veneers for Cabinet Work. It is also applied to Waterproofing Fabrics, Leather, Cloth, Book Binders' Cloth, Card Cloth, Writing Tablets, Bagatelle Balls and Pianoforte Keys, Gear and Friction Wheels, and Bearings for Machinery. Spinner's Bosses, Tubing; and as an Insulator and protector of Telegraph Wires.[20]

The change would appear to have been in name only.

Daniel Spill did break ground in one important new direction, one that, years later, would be of enormous significance in making celluloid an important material in its own right. The only public lecture or article on xylonite that is directly attributable to Spill was a talk delivered to a meeting of the London Photographic Society in December 1870. As might be suspected, here Spill turned his attention to the possible contributions that xylonite might make to photography. The most important application that he was then prepared to offer was the coating of photographic tents with colored xylonite solutions, at one and the same time waterproofing the tent and filtering out "actinic" rays of light, thus providing a sort of "safe-light" effect—a suggestion derived from Spill's long experience in his brother's waterproofing business. The future, however, held out greater possibilities: "On a future day I hope to offer a flexible and structureless substitute for the glass negative supports. My experiments in this direction are not at present sufficiently advanced to enable me to speak positively on the subject."[21] It would be too generous to suggest that Spill envisioned photographic film. That vision required an imaginative shift in form as much as in material and was more than two decades away. Still, it is only right to recognize that Spill possessed at least the germ of a very good and very important idea.

Unfortunately, Daniel Spill's operations met the same fate as that of the earlier Parkesine Company. By 1872 the Xylonite Company was in precarious condition, and two years later it folded.[22] Neither Spill's London Photographic Society talk nor the 1871 Xylonite circular mentioned a low price for xylonite. Presumably the Xylonite Company did avoid the earlier company's frantic pursuit of cheapness, and Spill's care to change the name of his product may also be attributed to his desire to avoid the taint caused by parkesine's low quality. Despite a better product, the Xylonite Company was no more successful at finding a market.

The Success of Celluloid

The commercial history of celluloid (and its predecessors) as thus far described in this chapter and the last has been one of failure. The collapse of the Parkesine and Xylonite companies and the difficulties of the Albany Billiard Ball and Dental Plate companies indicated that the problems of the new material in the market were no easier to solve than the problems in the laboratory. While the technical breakthrough in producing a successful plastic can be pinpointed as the discovery of the proper use of camphor, the commercial breakthroughs are not so easily defined. Solution of technical problems was clearly crucial and was the most important difference between the experience of celluloid and its English predecessors. But just as the failures of Parkes and Spill had more complex causes than chemistry, the ultimate success of the Hyatts and their partners was due to more than Hyatt's inventions.

The causes of the success of any new technology go beyond technical elements. They involve the presentation of the technology by those that control it (the producers) and the reception by those that use it (the consumers). Any complete understanding of the fate of a new technology must encompass the actions of both and their interaction in the market. The actions of producers are more complex than simple manufacture— they involve the determination of the roles which the technology is to fill, and that in turn involves the presentation of particular images, promises, and values. The way in which consumers respond to such presentations is the final determinant of economic success or failure; but just as producers do more than produce, consumers do more than buy. Or, to be more accurate, their buying has implications more complicated than simple cash flow and consumption.

How consumers respond to a new technology—what they eventually are willing to pay for—determines the ultimate economic role of that technology. Uncovering the pattern of consumer responses and the reasons for these responses is, unfortunately, a difficult historical problem, particularly in the case of a century-old product whose overall economic impact was relatively small. Even the most basic data for celluloid consumption are not available. It is impossible to say, for instance, just how many combs were made from celluloid or what proportion of knife handles were made of the new plastic. As for the real character of consumer reaction—how the material was perceived by those that worked with it and those that bought and used the products made from it—this was rarely, if ever, explicitly expressed.

On the other hand, there is enough evidence to allow some things to be said about how producers presented celluloid, how they sought out markets for the material, and, sometimes, how celluloid products fit into the context of traditional markets. The Celluloid Manufacturing Company and some of the companies that emulated it were eventually successful. It is possible to understand some of the basic characteristics of this success and hence to say some things about how a new material could be made a permanently acceptable and useful element of nineteenth-century technology. This is an important problem to address, for there is nothing in what has been said about celluloid so far that indicates what good it was, how it might be considered a bit of technological progress, how this first artificial plastic contributed anything to commercial enterprise, material life, or human welfare.

The remainder of this chapter will describe how the makers of celluloid responded to the problem of turning their new product into a useful commodity. This can be told primarily by dealing with the first years of the Celluloid Manufacturing Company, since it was by the efforts of this one company that celluloid finally became a permanently marketable material. Thanks to the difficult litigation that the company was forced to undergo with Daniel Spill, there is available a significant amount of data on the company's production and sales from the time that it was first established in Newark in 1872 to the middle of 1880, when court-ordered testimony was given regarding the company's operations. There is also information about the fabricating companies licensed by the Celluloid Manufacturing Company during its first decade. Since the company's policy very early was to make celluloid available to consumers only through manufacturers granted exclusive licenses for various products, the licenses of the company give a good picture of how the use of celluloid spread from product to product. The sorts of products ultimately made suggest what the celluloid manufacturers were trying to do with their product and how various characteristics of the product and of the articles made from it interacted to determine ultimate uses.

The success of the Celluloid Manufacturing Company after it set up its first plant in Newark was far from immediate. Indeed, in its first years the company sustained substantial losses, as Table 3.1 indicates. It must be cautioned, however, that these figures were provided by the company

Table 3.1

Celluloid Manufacturing Company
Gross Earnings, 1873–1879

Year	Receipts	Expenses	Loss/Profit
1873	$ 10,455.12	$ 58,446.83	$−47,991.71
1874	52,553.29	77,606.11	−25,052.82
1875	71,078.33	106,435.52	−35,357.19
1876	130,030.31	138,144.63	− 8,114.32
1877	172,366.97	147,901.98	+24,464.99
1878	176,917.06	142,165.49	+34,751.57
1879	290,992.03	219,947.39	+71,044.64

SOURCE: Exhibit B, "Master's Report," Spill v. Celluloid Mfg. Co. (Supreme Court), pp. 1062–63.

in a court action where it was desirable to understate profits as much as possible. Lawyers for Daniel Spill charged that the company's profits from 1876 to mid-1880 totaled at least $100,000 more than reported.[23] Nevertheless, not even they challenged the high losses claimed for the company's first years.

The total loss in company operations from 1873 to 1876 was $116,516. This was not due solely to difficulty in selling, but also to a sizable fire in 1875 and to the normally high capitalization costs that would be expected in the start-up of any sophisticated chemical industry. Enough is known about the first profitable years of the Celluloid Manufacturing Company to suggest the extent to which the costs of starting operations contributed to the early difficulties. Table 3.2 indicates the extent of the Celluloid Manufacturing Company's production from 1876 to 1879 and shows how the eventual profitability of the company resulted from drastically lowered costs rather than from exogenous increases in demand. While the

Table 3.2

Celluloid Manufacturing Company
Production, 1876–1879

Year	New Celluloid Produced (in pounds)	Cost of Production	Av. Cost per Pound	Av. Price per Pound
1876	67,060	$138,934.68	$2.060	$1.939
1877	101,095	147,950.74	1.463	1.704
1878	123,891	142,155.67	1.148	1.427
1879	212,921	220,036.61	1.033	1.366

SOURCE: Exhibit B, "Master's Report," Spill v. Celluloid Mfg. Co. (Supreme Court), pp. 1053–63.

cost of raw materials did decrease during this period—the cost of paper falling from $0.21 per pound in 1876 to $0.145 per pound in 1879 and that of alcohol from $2.156 a gallon in 1876 to $2.03 a gallon in 1879 (camphor remaining near $0.27 a pound)—this fall was not substantial enough to explain the halving of production costs in these four years.[24] The savings were probably due, instead, to improved mechanization, general economies of scale, and eventual reduction of capital outlay.

This period was the most important for establishing celluloid's basic price range. The average prices shown in Table 3.2 tend to hide the fact that celluloid was actually sold at a number of different prices, depending on form and quality. For example, in 1876 sheet celluloid could be bought for $2.75, $2.25, $2.00, $1.75, and $1.50 per pound. At that time most purchases were in the middle prices, but by 1880, when prices ranged from $2.25 to $1.25 per pound, the preponderance of consumption had shifted to the cheaper varieties.[25] This shift was probably a factor in the decline in average prices during this period. After 1880 data for prices and production are either meager or nonexistent. There is, however, some indication that the price of celluloid continued to decline slightly during the next decade. An inventory sheet found in the records of one of the Celluloid Manufacturing Company's major rivals suggests that a typical price for celluloid sheet in 1887 was $0.85 per pound.[26] This was, of course, under competitive conditions, and competition and volume production probably depressed celluloid prices. It is unlikely that celluloid got much cheaper than it was in the mid-1880s. U.S. Census data for 1919 gave the average value per pound of celluloid as $0.73.[27] Since at this time the volume of production was very much higher than it ever was in the nineteenth century, it is improbable that prices in that period were ever as low as the 1919 figure.

After the Celluloid Manufacturing Company began making a profit, its financial condition improved steadily, and it repaid its investors handsomely. For fourteen years after 1876, until the reorganization of the company in 1890, the annual dividends paid to stockholders averaged 34 percent of par.[28] The best record of the company's slow but steady rise to prosperity lies, not in corporate archives, which have not survived, but in the evaluations of credit reporters. As a new concern, dealing in a novel and untested product, the Celluloid Manufacturing Company came under careful scrutiny by the agents of America's chief credit referral firm, Dun, Barlow and Company (later R. G. Dun and Co., and finally Dun and Bradstreet). The periodic reports from the Newark agents, set down in the Dun ledgers, give a special insight into celluloid's climb to commercial respectability, as well as a unique glimpse at the kind of men who shepherded that climb.[29] The first report, dated 24 March 1873, followed an interview with president Marshall Lefferts, who explained the company's background and its business. The agent wrote, "They manufacture from Cotton Pulp a substitute for hard rubber, bone and ivory . . . used for a variety of purposes such as hairbrush backs, knife handles, &c." The most important information, however, dealt with the company's investments and financial health: "[They] claim to have $146,000 invested, a good deal of which has been spent in experiments. Claims to have an active Capital of $40,000 & that no stock is to be had, would not sell that which [Lefferts] owns and controls at 150%." Finally, of course, the creditworthiness of the new business was evaluated. Since "some good names [were] connected with the organization" and all bills were promptly paid in cash, there was little to question on that score.

Over the following months and years the Dun, Barlow reports on the celluloid manufacturer chronicled early difficulties and eventual success. On 16 June 1874, the entire entry was, "Not yet doing much bus[iness] but believed safe." A couple of weeks later, an extensive evaluation was filed, describing the company's mode of operations: "[They] are believed to have a gd. & eventually a profitable patent, are licensing [a] firm to manufr. specialities under their patent material & tho this income can't yet be said to be remunerative it is bel[ieved] it will eventually become so." This optimistic outlook was sustained in the next report, dated 9

January 1875: "Their assets consist of materials, machy. & patents[,] the latter deemed of consid[erable] val[ue] whose g[oo]d pros[pects] to grow more so, as the utility of Celluloid appears to be so decided as to allow it to be used in a gt. variety of directions & of course the prosperity of the company increases in proportion to the increased use of this peculiar material." The report sent in from Newark six months later stated simply, "no change," but in September, the agent filed this brief but ominous message: "Their factory was destroyed last night by fire. Mr. Hyatt, Treas., places the loss at $150,000. Insurance $45,000, making loss of $105,000, further particulars soon." Only a few hours later, the additional information came in that the company would "go on with the bus. as soon as they can get accommodations. Investigation shows the loss to be abt. $100,000 & Ins[urance] $58,000." Nothing could have better recorded the celluloid company's faith in the future of its product.

The Dun, Barlow agents used information from a variety of sources, including the company's annual report. In January 1875, they revealed that the capitalization had been increased to $500,000, of which $115,000 had been paid in in cash and the remainder "for patents and other ppty. necessary for the business." Liabilities were only $6,000. The following January's report revealed that cash invested totaled $167,800 and liabilities had risen to $30,110—presumably due to the previous September's disastrous fire. By June 1876, however, the credit rating was clearly positive, and six months later, in January 1877, the picture drawn by the agent's report was positively rosy. The company was "doing well & believed to be making money." Things looked even better in July, when the company was reported to be "G[oin]g on all right. D[oin]g a large extensive bus[iness]. Are now arranging to extend the bus. to France & other foreign countries. Their stock here is held above par and bought by financial men." From this point on, the Dun, Barlow records show nothing but high regard for the Celluloid Manufacturing Company's business, even while reporting such setbacks as another factory fire (in January 1880). In April 1880, the company was said to be paying 25 percent dividends, and the October 1881 report stated that the "stock is worth so much that it can hardly be quoted—two to four hundred dollars have been offered for it," par being $100. The company's prosperity and creditworthiness having been firmly established, in subsequent years few reports were filed, and these all simply confirmed the happy state of affairs: "Very safe money making concern" (August 1882); "profitable corporation doing a large business & steadily making money" (March 1885); "very strong, wealthy concern" (November 1887). By 1890, the credit rating of the Celluloid Manufacturing Company had risen to "A1"—Dun's highest.[30] Through intelligent technical development combined with conservative business practices, the first celluloid manufacturers achieved in less than twenty years a degree of commercial respectability that could well be envied by many of the other technical pioneers of late-nineteenth-century America.

The Strategy of Success

The causes of this success were more complex than simply a better understanding of the technical requirements of a good pyroxylin plastic and the steady support of financial backers. The Americans approached the problem of finding a market for celluloid in ways that were significantly different from those of the English. The experience of the Hyatts with billiard balls and then with dental plates reflected one crucial difference. Instead of presenting their material as a broad-ranging substitute for a wide variety of different substances in a great diversity of applications, the Hyatts cautiously tried celluloid in one special market and then another. The results were mixed—in fact, at the start they were generally poor—but they provided the basis for judging the strengths and weaknesses of the new material and for more accurately predicting its potential in other markets.

It is possible to trace many of the steps taken by the celluloid makers in their gradual but steady accumulation of outlets. As pointed out in Chapter 2, the use of celluloid for billiard balls (or at least for the coating of the balls) and for dental plates never ceased entirely, despite the limitations of celluloid in both of these products. Until 1873 dental plates were the main outlet for celluloid. In December 1872 the Celluloid Manufacturing Company opened a factory in Newark to produce more diverse goods.[31] Company president Marshall Lefferts testified that the principal products in 1873 were dental plates, knife handles, and harness trimmings.[32] The next several years saw a slow diversification, the pattern of which indicated a great concern on the part of the Celluloid Manufacturing Company that their product be used only in ways that reflected well on the properties of celluloid.

After the experience of the company with dental plates, it was decided that the Newark factory would be used largely for producing unfabricated celluloid, primarily but not exclusively in the form of sheets. The making of consumer products from celluloid would be the business of licensees, some of whom would be established businesses that had been persuaded to use celluloid and others of whom would be firms set up with the encouragement of the Celluloid Manufacturing Company but generally without financial ties. There exist two separate lists of licenses for the use of celluloid granted by the Newark company in the 1870s. The licenses on these lists document the growing applications of celluloid.

One of the lists of licenses was part of testimony given under oath in the *Spill* v. *Celluloid Manufacturing Company* litigation in 1880. Because this list is chronological, it presents a clear picture of when various celluloid products were developed. An abbreviated version of this list is given in Table 3.3; the date given is the earliest associated with a particular license. These dates do not necessarily represent the precise beginnings of the manufacture of various celluloid products. On the other

Table 3.3

Licenses Issued by the Celluloid
Manufacturing Company, 1872–1880

Date of Issue	Licensee	Final Product or Form of Celluloid Supplied*
1 Oct. 1872	Samuel S. White	Dental plate blanks
12 Feb. 1873	Celluloid Harness Trimming Co.	Sheets
26 Jan. 1874	Edward C. Penfield	Truss pads
20 Nov. 1874	Meriden Cutlery Co.	Knife handles
21 Nov. 1874	I. Smith Hyatt (later, Celluloid Brush Co.)	Brushes
1 Sept. 1875	Emery Wheel Co.	Emery wheels
18 Sept. 1875	Spencer Optical Mfg. Co.	
22 Dec. 1875	Celluloid Novelty Co.	Finished shapes
1 Mar. 1877	Albany Billiard Ball Co.	Sheets
9 Mar. 1878	Celluloid Waterproof Cuff and Collar Co.	Thin sheets
23 Oct. 1878	Celluloid Hat & Trimming Co.	Sheet from rolls
31 Oct. 1878	Celluloid Fancy Goods Co.	Fancy articles
30 Nov. 1878	Celluloid Shoe Protector Co.	
12 Dec. 1878	Celluloid Piano Key Co.	Sheets
1 Apr. 1879	Celluloid Veneer Co.	Thin veneers
1 Mar. 1880	Celluloid Surgical Instrument Co.	

*As specified by the license.
SOURCE: "Master's Report," Spill v. Celluloid Mfg. Co., pp. 998–1006. Edward C. Penfield's product was not given in this list but was taken from William F. Ford, *The Industrial Interests of Newark, N.J.* (New York: Van Arsdale & Co., 1874), pp. 21–22.

hand, the policy of the Celluloid Manufacturing Company was such that
the issuance of a license generally did indicate the start of commercial
production of a product or a particular class of products.

All of the firms on this list, with the exception of the Celluloid Brush
Company, had no direct connection with the Celluloid Manufacturing
Company besides its license. The Manufacturing Company's involvement in the Brush Company consisted in the former's holding a one-
twentieth share of the stock of the latter. According to testimony, this was
compensation for the "results of [the Manufacturing Company's] experiments in making combs, including the dies and other machinery
which [it] had purchased for the purpose of moulding and cutting
combs," which the Manufacturing Company gave to the new firm.[33] The
product line of the Celluloid Brush Company included combs and mirrors
as well as brushes, and was the outgrowth of intensive product development by the Hyatts and their co-workers. Other licensee companies, while
without direct corporate links, frequently included overlapping personnel
or interlocking boards. The Celluloid Novelty Company, for example,
had Marshall Lefferts on its board and one of his sons serving as
treasurer. The fact that the Celluloid Manufacturing Company itself
largely avoided finished products should not obscure the fact that the
company had a great deal to do with the development of the products it
eventually licensed.

The key contrast between the picture suggested by the list of licenses
and that presented by the experience of the English companies was the
gradualism practiced by the Newark manufacturers. It seems natural
that the first license on the list should be to the S. S. White Company, the
Philadelphia dental supply firm that had handled the output of the
Albany Dental Plate Company. The Harness Trimming Company was
the first of numerous small firms established in Newark to work celluloid
into marketable forms. It was first set up at the same address as the
Manufacturing Company and made rings, hooks, buckles, rosettes, and
other harness trimmings, competing largely with the much more expensive ivory or the somewhat unsatisfactory (in appearance if not in performance) hard rubber.[34] Such a product represented a humble but effective
way of challenging more traditional materials.

Penfield and Company was a Philadelphia medical supply house which
may have been influenced by the S. S. White Company in trying out
celluloid for the manufacture of truss pads and coatings for truss springs.
Here too, celluloid was competing with hard rubber, and it would have to
be considered a luxury item, preferable for its better flesh coloring and its
flexibility in cold weather.[35] Knife handles and brushes and combs had
been among the few important products of the Parkesine and Xylonite

companies, and their early appearance in celluloid was to be expected. In cutlery, celluloid simply offered another material in a field that already had a great number. The ease with which celluloid could be colored and worked made it a very attractive replacement for such natural materials as bone, horn, shell, and ivory; and as late as 1938 it was reported that cutlery manufacturers were "emphatic" in maintaining the importance of celluloid to their trade.[36]

The involvement of the Celluloid Manufacturing Company in product development was extensive. Between 1869 and 1891 there were issued to John Wesley Hyatt sixty-one patents relating to the manufacturing and working of celluloid. While many of Hyatt's patents involved techniques and machines for celluloid production and finishing, a number were for the making of specific articles, among them collars, cuffs, and combs. Other important individuals in the Celluloid Manufacturing Company took out patents for new celluloid products. Marshall C. Lefferts, son of the Marshall Lefferts who had directed the company during its first years in Newark and later president of the company himself, was granted patents for such things as syringes, spoons and forks, dolls, stays, and ice pitchers.[37] As might be expected, many of the processes developed by the Celluloid Manufacturing Company and by other celluloid producers were of little or no commercial importance, but the very fact of their patenting indicated that product development was always important to these companies.

All but two of the companies licensed by the Celluloid Manufacturing Company to fabricate the material were specialized, making and selling a very narrow range of consumer goods. Specialization of product meant both specialization of labor—the ability to recruit and employ workers skilled in producing a traditional product like combs or piano keys—and specialization of marketing—the opportunity to compete with traditional materials on carefully selected ground. Instead of being introduced to a multiplicity of markets as a suitable replacement for a wide range of un-differentiated materials, celluloid was presented as a good replacement for bone in knife handles at one time, and a substitute for ivory in piano keys at another. The usefulness of the material as a substitute could be carefully judged by both consumer and producer as each product was introduced. Sometimes the effort would be a failure: the Celluloid Hat and Trimming Company was never able to sell its product, nor was the Shoe Protector Company. In other cases this step-by-step approach produced surprising successes, as in the case of the Waterproof Cuff and Collar Company, which was able to make a novelty into an acceptable fashion that died only with the disappearance of removable collars and cuffs altogether.

At first glance there appear to have been two celluloid fabricators whose products were not narrowly defined: the Celluloid Novelty Company and the Celluloid Fancy Goods Company. Indeed, their products were varied, but there was in fact a logic both in their use of celluloid's properties and in the marketing of their products that was coherent and precise, and that had a major role in shaping the image and application of plastics. The best account of the articles produced by these two companies comes from the other important list of the Celluloid Manufacturing Company licenses. This consists of two ledger books, titled *Licenses, Contracts, and Patents*, listing various agreements made by the company in the years 1872–78.[38] The index to these volumes summarizes the products that the Novelty and the Fancy Goods Companies were licensed to produce: for the Celluloid Novelty Company,

armlets	watch chains	shawl pins
breast pins	earrings	sleeve buttons
bracelets	jewelry	shirt studs
crosses	necklaces	scarf pins and
charms	pendants	rings

and for the Celluloid Fancy Goods Company,

checkers	bows, scarves	tape measures
cribbage boards	card and jewelry	thermometers
dice boxes	receivers	(small, fancy)
key rings	saltcellars	
neckties	soap dishes	
	thimbles	

It is easy to think of items, such as varieties of buttons, calling cards, or razor handles, that were made of celluloid and that might have fallen under the purview of one or the other of these companies and yet do not appear here. The lists are sufficient, however, to convey a general image of the variety of small articles being made out of celluloid by 1878.

Such a diversity of products brings to mind the products of the Parkesine and Xylonite companies, but the Newark companies did not have the problems of the Hackney Wick manufacturers. Besides the technical superiority of their material, the marketing strategy of the celluloid makers helped them to avoid the fate of the English firms. A closer look at the lists of products reveals that all of the articles sold by the Novelty Company were items of personal ornament, and thus could be marketed together through fairly narrow channels. Cheap jewelry was not a new idea in the late nineteenth century; and celluloid items, despite their diverse forms, could be presented as new sorts of inexpensive ornament, superior in appearance to hard rubber or other cheap substances, and considerably less expensive than coral or amber or pearl.

The same point could be made about the products of the Fancy Goods Company; despite the apparent diversity of articles, they fit easily into a well-defined segment of the market—fancy hardwares. It might not be so easy to determine what natural substances celluloid was generally replacing in such goods; the possibilities included wood, glass, and metal, as well as the high-priced semiprecious substances. A license was not issued to the Celluloid Fancy Goods Company until late 1878, almost six years after celluloid production began in Newark. By this time celluloid may have received enough public exposure to be considered a material in its own right, not simply an imitation of something more natural and more precious. It would be going too far, however, to suggest that celluloid had by this time become truly independent of the need to be essentially imitative. Even in the fancy goods trade, the material was prepared carefully so that it would, in most instances, suggest a familiar natural substance. The breakaway from imitation could be finally achieved only by a breakaway from replacement, by the creation of a new product made possible by the new material. This achievement lay years in the future.

In the meantime considerable effort was expended in imitating a wide variety of natural substances. The first and most important imitation was of ivory. Whatever the difficulty may have been in making a satisfactory celluloid billiard ball, for other uses of ivory the material was eminently suitable. A successful ivory imitation had to imitate not only the color of the natural substance, but also the graining. With celluloid this could be done by putting sheets of varying shades of white or beige and of varying thicknesses together, bending and folding the stacked sheets and repeatedly putting them through heated rollers.[39] A look at a collection of old celluloid objects, such as that in the Smithsonian Institution's National Museum of American History, shows an overwhelming preponderance of imitation ivory. This extends even to many articles that would never have been made of natural ivory, such as calling cards and vases.

This disposition towards the ivory form was both because of and despite the versatility of celluloid. Some newly emerging materials, like hard rubber, were difficult to make in attractive colors because of their natural dark coloring. Hence, black became the color associated with hard-rubber products, and even jewelry was made in shiny black hard rubber. Rubber was forced to create its own image. Celluloid was under no such restraints; it could be very easily made to imitate ivory or coral or any of a wide variety of natural substances. Unlike natural materials, it could also be colored. It could be made in any color of the rainbow, in a wide range of transparent and opaque forms. Freed from the constraints that hampered manufacturers of materials like hard rubber, celluloid makers found it easier to popularize their products in forms both familiar and admired, rather than exploit the creative possibilities of their material. This was true not only in the first years of celluloid manufacture, but for decades thereafter, even when rival plastics began to appear.

While ivory was certainly the most popular imitative form of celluloid, it was by no means the only one. Celluloid horn was also made, requiring, like ivory, special processing to produce hornlike striations and marbling. Tortoiseshell was one of celluloid's most important imitations, in part because it could be done so well and in part because natural tortoiseshell was rapidly becoming scarce. Numerous methods were used to make imitation pearl and mother-of-pearl from celluloid, as well as coral and amber imitations, the latter being widely used for pipestems despite the flammability of the material. Marble and onyx could also be mimicked by celluloid, as could almost any decorative mineral.[40] The production of beautiful effects with celluloid, almost all of them imitative, was the subject of innumerable experiments and patents in the last quarter of the nineteenth century. The result of these efforts, however, often was less to prepare celluloid for the direct substitution of the imitated material in some particular use than it was to give the plastic a familiar and readily accepted appearance regardless of the object that was actually made from it. Hence celluloid calling cards looking like ivory or tortoiseshell were not intended so much to suggest real ivory or tortoiseshell cards—such things did not exist—but rather, to produce plastic cards in an indisputably acceptable form.

Imitation and Substitution

Making celluloid into an imitation of a natural substance was not done solely to substitute for the traditional material, but direct substitution was frequent. The extent to which such substitution did occur is not easy to determine. In some cases the evidence is flatly contradictory. For instance, imitation ivory piano keys made from celluloid were generally very satisfactory, and the company set up in 1878 to manufacture celluloid keys was successful. In a patent suit brought in 1882 to defend John Wesley Hyatt's patent on celluloid piano keys, evidence was accepted by the court to the effect that celluloid piano keys "drove out ivory and supplanted it almost entirely, . . . though ivory sets were sold cheaper than celluloid from 1880-1."[41] On the other hand, it was reported in 1916 that in a normal year (the example being 1913), the amount of celluloid

Table 3.4

Prices of Combs in the Late Nineteenth Century

Date	Celluloid	Ivory	Rubber	Horn	Shell
		Ehrich Bros., New York City			
Summer 1877	$1.40	$2.85–5.00			$1.40
Fall 1879	.45 & .65		$ .08–.75		
Fall 1885	.10– .25		.07– .65	$ .05–.25	
		B. Altman & Co., New York City			
1882–83	.48 & .60	1.75–4.00	.10–.50	.25–.70	$1.75–4.00
1888–89	.13– .30		.10–.45	.28–.50	
1892–93	.13– .30		.10–.45	.28–.55	
1912	.50–1.25				
		Spelman Bros., New York City			
Sept. 1883	4.50/doz.		1.00/doz.	1.00/doz	
Nov. 1885	1.10/doz.		10.80/gross	10.50/gross	
Jan. 1888	.65/doz.		.46–2.18/doz.	.30–.83/doz.	
Jan. 1888 (fine)	.75–.85/doz.	1.25–2.37/doz.	.19– .83/doz.	.22–.62/doz.	
July 1889	.40–.95/doz.		.37–2.14/doz.	.30–.85/doz.	

By Size

Size (in.)	White Xylonite (per doz.)	Stained Horn (per doz.)	White Horn (per doz.)	Vulcanite (per doz.)
		Lynch & Co., London, Jan. 1889		
7 x 1.25	7s. 6d.	4s. 6d. & 6s. 6d.	4s. & 9s.	3s. 6d.
8 x 1.50	10s.	4s. 6d. & 6s. 6d.	12s. 6d. (best)	10s.
7.50 x 1.50	8s. 9d.	4s. & 5s. 9d.	7s. & 11s. 6d.	5s. 9d.

used for piano keys amounted to only 8 percent of the total of ivory or ivorylike material used for keys.[42] The difference in cost between ivory and celluloid keys was indeed not very significant. The Sears, Roebuck *Catalog* for spring 1896 offered numerous pianos for sale, all of them with ivory keys except for the cheapest, which was supplied with "ivory or celluloid keys as desired."[43] This easy interchange between ivory and celluloid suggests that, insofar as this product was concerned, little distinction in price was made. Which customers actually preferred is another question, but it can be guessed that, because of its exclusive use on the more expensive pianos (at least of the sort sold by Sears), ivory was the usual choice.

The role that celluloid played in the other markets can be understood somewhat better. One of the most widely disseminated and readily identifiable celluloid products was the comb. The general relationship between celluloid and the comb industry will be discussed at length below, but the data on the prices of combs can serve to illustrate how celluloid developed an economic niche. By the last quarter of the nineteenth century, combs were made of a number of different materials: horn, ivory, hard rubber, tortoiseshell, and celluloid. The price lists and catalogs of a number of New York City comb outlets in the late nineteenth century, studied carefully, reveal the relative prices of celluloid articles. Because combs were made in a wide variety of styles, shapes, and sizes, it is difficult to compare prices accurately, but patterns do emerge if one looks at a number of sources.

Table 3.4 summarizes the results of a survey of three New York City dry goods outlets, two retail and the last wholesale. Also included is a summary of prices for different sizes of combs as listed in the catalog of a London wholesaler. This last is included because it is one of the few lists that consistently gives the sizes of the items being offered. Together, these lists suggest the difficulty of making simple comparisons in the prices of different kinds of combs. Nevertheless, there is enough here to indicate that celluloid assumed a place somewhere between the most expensive and the cheapest of materials for combs. Ivory combs, as might be expected, were always costlier than combs made of other materials, except perhaps for tortoiseshell, which was generally not only as expensive as ivory but also scarcer. On the other hand, rubber combs were consistently cheaper than celluloid, and hence there were often available very fancy or large combs of rubber, costing more than the most expensive comb available in celluloid. The cheapest rubber combs, however, were always cheaper than the lowest-priced celluloid ones, and these appear to have been more comparable in style and size. The best confirmation of this comes from the English prices shown in Table 3.4, where rubber combs of the same size as celluloid ones were sometimes less than half the price of the celluloid.

The relationship between the economic position of celluloid in the market and that of horn was a bit more complicated. As a by-product of beef production, horn was generally a cheap material in the late nineteenth century, but only in certain sizes and colors. If horn was processed to clarify it, it cost more than unprocessed horn. If a horn comb was fairly large, it would have what might seem a disproportionately higher price because large, good pieces of horn were much harder to come by than smaller pieces. In other words, horn was a good example of the limitations presented by a common natural substance. Within certain naturally defined limits, horn could be cheap and plentiful. Outside of those limits of size and color, it became much more costly, and the competitive advantage of a substance not so limited became manifest.

Whatever may have been the advantages of celluloid over other materials used for combs, they did not show themselves in the final products in any overwhelming way. Celluloid's displacement of other materials was not radical. It was not a revolutionary, cheap substance. It set no important new fashions. It possessed no remarkable advantages in utility. Yet, from the pattern of the prices and the availability of celluloid combs in the 1880s, it is apparent that the appeal of the material to consumers was significant. It did establish itself as an important alternative material. This was partly due to its adoption by producers on account of its ease of working and dependability of supply. But even before its widespread adoption by the comb-makers, celluloid established an appeal to consumers. Its price, while not always the lowest, was unquestionably competitive with most comb materials. Its appearance was no great departure from fashion or tradition and was (or could be) generally attractive. Celluloid was a sound material for combs. It warped no more easily than most of the other comb materials. Its feel was comfortable, and its combination of flexibility and durability was well within the range customary for combs. Celluloid's place in the comb market was due largely to its likeness to traditional materials, not to its differences. This was a crucial characteristic of celluloid's success. The new material did not change markets; it adapted itself to them.

The Market Niche

The successful introduction of celluloid was not an easy accomplishment. The problems of the makers of parkesine and xylonite best illustrated the necessity for the solution of both technical and commercial problems before a product like celluloid could be viable. The Hyatts' difficulties in establishing billiard balls and dental plates as important celluloid products taught them the importance of recognizing both the technological and the economic limitations of their invention. To make celluloid successful it was necessary not only to discover the chemical and mechanical means to make a stable and workable pyroxylin plastic, but also to determine the useful properties of such a material. Celluloid did not have the same elasticity as ivory or the durability of hard rubber, but it did have a versatility of coloring and ease of working that could be used advantageously. Celluloid could never, under ordinary conditions, be as cheap as rubber or the cheapest horn, but it could be made much more attractive than they. It was in terms of traditional materials and traditional products that celluloid had to be defined, and the success of the Hyatts was in finding an economically viable definition.

Within a few years of its introduction in America, celluloid had clearly assumed the role of an imitative material. This was the result not so much of the origins of the Hyatts' invention in their efforts to replace ivory in billiard balls, but of the manufacturers' perceptions of the most direct ways to exploit celluloid's decorative versatility. Even where celluloid products went beyond imitation, as in waterproof collars and cuffs, the final form of the product was carefully made to resemble a traditional material—in this case, the stitches and weave of linen were reproduced throughout the celluloid collar.[44] Why should a manufacturer undertake the difficult task of trying to create new fashions in such fashion-sensitive products as collars or combs if his material allowed him to imitate traditional products? Later perhaps, customers could be attracted to such products made from transparent or brightly-dyed plastics, but not in the beginning. Hence, from the start, "plastic" usually meant "imitation."

Also established in these first years of American manufacture was the basic price identification of celluloid. This was something that Alexander Parkes and his partners were unable to do. Even without complete knowledge of how important camphor was in making a good pyroxylin plastic, Parkes was able to produce a useful material if care and skill went into its manufacture. But there was early pressure to produce parkesine at "a shilling a pound," and hence lower-quality materials and less care went into the product, resulting in an often worthless substance. The makers of celluloid, despite their superior technical knowledge, could have made the same mistake if they had insisted on trying to make a very cheap material. This was not their object, however, as is most clearly shown by the effort to market celluloid in competition with hard rubber for dental plates. The difficulty that the material experienced in this market showed the Hyatts and their partners that celluloid would generally have to be price-competitive. Therefore, the material was established as an intermediate substance—never as cheap as rubber and a few other materials, but definitely cheaper than the natural materials that it imitated so well. Here too celluloid set a precedent for the modern plastics—rarely the cheapest alternative (pound for pound), but cheap enough to provide an economical substitute for many traditional substances.

The products that established celluloid as an economic commodity were not novel. The form that celluloid took in the market was not startlingly new. Individual features that celluloid offered in competition with other substances were not of great importance: there was usually something else that was cheaper, and yet another that was finer in appearance or feel. But celluloid, by dint of its good imitation of finer things, of its durability in normal use, of its modest cost, and of its versatility in size, shape, color, and design, became an accepted part of the material life of industrial and domestic society.

4

Applications, Impacts, and Images

AFTER ITS first years of struggling to find viable roles in the marketplace, the celluloid industry entered a period of active and robust adolescence. In the years from 1875 to the end of the century, the technical, economic, and cultural dimensions of the new technology emerged. These dimensions were shaped by entrepreneurs and capitalists seeking to exploit new opportunities, by communities struggling to adapt themselves to change, by journalists and publicists eager to interpret the novelty for their readers or to promote it to potential customers, and, finally, by the characteristics of celluloid itself, as its uses and failings became known through experience. This adolescence not only shaped the character of the mature technology, but it also left a legacy of impressions and images to which plastics are still heir in twentieth-century culture.

The most basic characteristic of the celluloid industry in the late nineteenth century was its increasing size and complexity. Its initial success in a Newark factory spawned emulation and competition, in America and abroad. Size and competition naturally changed the conditions under which manufacturers sought to create and hold markets. Growth also brought with it certain consequences that could not have been foreseen in the infant stages of the industry. Some of these effects were very localized —changes wrought in traditional communities that felt compelled to adapt themselves to the new technology—but they were sometimes so striking that their small geographic range was less important than their social and economic implications. Others were the product of promotion —of the efforts to make celluloid successful by shaping its use and image to the requirements of the most promising markets. These efforts left long-lasting imprints on the perception of the new material as well as on its sales. In hindsight, the implications of what the celluloid makers and sellers were doing can be sorted out, but it is well to remember that few of them were perceived at the time.

A Growing Industry

Among the new categories of products reported in the United States *Census of Manufactures* for 1880 was "Celluloid and Celluloid Goods." The *Census* reported five establishments under that heading in the state of New Jersey and one in New York, producing products valued at $1,261,540 for the census year.[1] The 1890 *Census of Manufactures* reported twelve firms in the celluloid industry, only three of which were in New Jersey. The New Jersey companies, however, accounted for more than two-thirds of the total value of celluloid products produced: $1,721,773 out of $2,575,736.[2] Taking into account the price deflation of the 1880s of about 12 percent, these figures indicated considerable growth. On the other hand, this growth should not be exaggerated. For one thing, census figures included not only the value of the celluloid produced, but also the added value of the fabricated products. The celluloid industry was in fact still quite small. Compare, for example, the 1880 *Census* figures for other industries, such as "Billiard Tables and Materials" ($2,289,758), "Paper Collars and Cuffs" ($1,582,571), and "Combs" ($951,395). While celluloid could therefore by no means be called a major industry by 1880 or even 1890, it was clearly an expanding one.

Numerous companies were set up in the 1870s and 1880s to make some version of a pyroxylin plastic. The confused patent situation surrounding celluloid prevented the Celluloid Manufacturing Company from exercising any patent control over the industry. In 1877 a Schenectady, New York, manufacturer set up a firm to produce what was variously called "coraline," "coroline," or "coralline," a pyroxylin plastic colored to look like coral and intended for jewelry and corset stays.[3] The Lignoid Fancy Article Manufacturing Company was first established in Newark, but by 1880 it had moved to Newburyport, Massachusetts (a move associated, it may be assumed, with the comb industry in that region), and later became the Fiberloid Company.[4] In 1881 or 1882, an American entrepreneur took out a license to work Daniel Spill's patents in the United States and set up the American Zylonite Company in North Adams, Massachusetts. It was this company that was to have benefitted from Daniel Spill's patent suits. When Spill's patents were invalidated in 1886, the company found itself in financial difficulty, and the Celluloid Manufacturing Company absorbed it in 1890–91.[5]

This proliferation continued for many decades. By 1920 a list of pyroxylin plastics that had had brief lives in the marketplace read from A to X: Argonite, Alberite, Apiroid, Boroid, Camphoid, Celluline, Cellulodine,

Cellulosine, Crystalloid, Dermatoid, Elastozon, Exonite, Histoloid, Hyaline, Ivorine, Ivoride, Lithoxyle, Parckut, Prostine, Phibrolithoid, Pyroxlid, Setolid, Satolite, Securite, Sternoid, Steroylin, Suberit, Vegetalin, Vitroloid, Xylamile, and Xylonith.[6] Most of these products were very like celluloid, but while patent restrictions on the material had been lifted, the trademark protection for the name "celluloid" remained intact.

The most important American manufacturer of celluloid next to the original Hyatt company was a company set up in northern New Jersey in 1881 as the Merchant's Manufacturing Company, makers of "pasbosene." In 1883 this firm became the Cellonite Company, and its product was similarly renamed.[7] A new plant was built in Arlington, New Jersey, in 1885, and the company again renamed, this name as the Arlington Manufacturing Company (later simplified to the Arlington Company). The product, identical to celluloid, was finally labeled "pyralin." The new company experienced great technical difficulties in its first years and survived only by recruiting skilled workmen in 1891 from the recently closed plant of the American Zylonite Company.[8] Like the celluloid manufacturers, the makers of cellonite/pyralin organized themselves into both material producers and fabricators of final products. Thus the incorporation papers for the Arlington Collar and Cuff Company, taken out in 1886, specify: "The objects for which the company is formed are to manufacture waterproof collars and cuffs from cellonite or other plastic material, and other useful or ornamental articles, and to sell the same."[9] Just as in the case of the Newark pioneers, all of the Arlington enterprises were reorganized in the 1890s under the corporate umbrella of the Arlington Company. The parallels in the experiences of the two New Jersey manufacturers extended even to accidents, for only a few years after it was built, the plant of the Arlington Manufacturing Company was destroyed by an explosion and fire. This was only a temporary setback, but it was another vivid reminder of the hazards of pyroxylin manufacture.[10]

In 1890 the Celluloid Manufacturing Company attempted to absorb its most important competitors as well as a number of the satellite companies that it had fostered. Hence, the Celluloid Company was organized on 1 January 1891, made up of the Celluloid Manufacturing Company, the Celluloid Novelty Company, the Celluloid Brush Company, the American Zylonite Company, and a few smaller plastics producers.[11] The Arlington Company was not taken over and thus became the Celluloid Company's most important rival. The extent to which these two firms controlled the American market was reflected in an unsigned letter sent in

1892 or 1893 from the offices of the Arlington Company to the Celluloid
Company. Part of the letter read:

> Would it not be well for arrangements to be made for a representative from
> your Company to meet one from ours with a view to adjusting the prices
> and terms for the sale of waterproof collars and cuffs for the year 1893. There
> are, as you are aware, only you and ourselves making and controlling these
> goods and it seems to us unnecessary to sell at the low prices now being ob-
> tained.[12]

It is not known whether the companies did engage in price-fixing, but the
fact that it would have been easy and possibly desirable suggests the extent to which the New Jersey firms then controlled the market. The Arlington Company ceased independent existence in 1915, when it was purchased by E. I. du Pont de Nemours and Company, which continued to
produce "pyralin" for many years thereafter.[13]

European Foundations

It was not long after the establishment of celluloid production in Newark
that interest was shown in Europe in having the new technology set up
there. In 1875 the Hyatts approached potential European backers and
met with some success.[14] In that year the Compagnie Franco-Americaine
was established at Stains, outside Paris, manufacturing not only celluloid
but also soft and hard rubber.[15] The French company, operating with the
Hyatt patents, later became the Compagnie Française du Celluloid and
was for several years the only producer of raw celluloid on the
Continent.[16] In 1878 a German rubber-comb manufacturer, Magnus and
Company of Berlin, started up production of celluloid. The enterprise
was plagued by technical difficulties, however, and the works were
destroyed by fire, not to be rebuilt.[17] Later that same year a successful
celluloid fabrication plant was put into operation at Offenbach, near
Frankfurt, and two years later the first successful celluloid production
plant in Germany was established by the Rheinischen Hartgum-
miwaarenfabrik (later, the Rheinische Gummi- und Celluloid Fabrik) at
Mannheim. But explosions also plagued that factory, and legal restrictions were placed on its operations.[18] The Continental celluloid efforts
were often linked to hard-rubber manufacture. For example, the primary
product of the Mannheim factory, even before making celluloid, was rubber combs.

The story of celluloid in Britain was, of course, colored by the unhappy
experience of Parkes and Spill. In 1875 the Hyatts caught the attention of
L. P. Merriam, an American living in England. Negotiations for Merriam to establish the manufacture of celluloid in Britain under the Hyatt

patents fell through, but Merriam's interest in the new material led him to look up Daniel Spill. In the spring of 1876, Merriam went into business with Spill at Spill's works in suburban London. Initially the new British Xylonite Company was hardly more successful than its predecessors had been, limping along for years trying to market celluloid (for that is what xylonite now was) jewelry and combs. The somewhat class-conscious British market may have been less susceptible to the appeal of a cheap fancy comb than American or Continental consumers. The breakthrough came in 1885 with the decision of British Xylonite to go into the production of collars and cuffs. These products were clear successes, achieving a sort of middle-class acceptability and an appeal to practicality. Unlike the other major industrialized countries, Britain had only one major celluloid producer, a lineal descendant of the enterprises of Parkes and Spill.[19]

By 1890 the celluloid industry was firmly established in the United States, Britain, France, and Germany. It was not until after the First World War that other countries took up the manufacture. In its overall economic impact, celluloid was of no greater significance abroad than it was in the United States. In terms of local importance, however, the new industry could have very great consequences for specific industries and regions. The uses of celluloid abroad did not differ markedly from those in America. While often identified as an American product (celluloid collars and cuffs were often referred to in Europe as "American linen"), by the end of the century celluloid was very much an international commodity.

Combmaking in Leominster and Oyonnax: Celluloid and Change

As its use spread from product to product and from place to place, celluloid effected change. Often the changes were minor—introducing new colors for toys, making spectacle frames more varied, or providing cheaper dice for gamblers—but sometimes the changes were quite significant within their context. The best example of the impact that celluloid could have on traditional industries and their dependent communities was in the manufacture of combs. Not only did the new material upset old craft ways in combmaking, but it led to radical changes in the economic bases of combmaking towns. The significance of celluloid's impact can be drawn in particularly sharp relief in this instance because of the extraordinary parallel history of two widely separated towns, Leominster, in central Massachusetts, and Oyonnax, in the Jura of southeastern France.

Wood, bone, and ivory were for centuries the most common comb materials, but the use of metal, horn, shell, and even reeds is also very old. Like so many similar crafts, combmaking established during the Middle Ages and the early modern period traditional patterns of working and organization that lasted into the nineteenth century. Like some other crafts, also, combmaking became centered in a few locations, which grew into specialized manufacturing centers, supplying their particular sort of goods to a widespread, often national, market. Leominster and Oyonnax were two such centers in the mid-nineteenth century. The introduction of celluloid had an extraordinary impact on combmaking and on these two towns—an impact that highlighted both the problems and the opportunities presented by the introduction of a new material into a traditional manufacture.

Before the nineteenth century, the combmakers of Oyonnax largely used boxwood, from which they made highly polished combs. About the turn of the century, the hornlike material in the hoofs of horses and cattle (*ergot*) began to replace wood, and after 1820 this, in turn, began to be replaced by true horn. After 1848, horn was used in combmaking to the exclusion of almost every other substance.[20] The making of combs in America was established in northeastern Massachusetts in the mid-eighteenth century, moving out from the Newburyport region later in the century to towns like Leominster in the interior. Here tortoiseshell and horn were always the dominant materials, though not to the total exclusion of ivory or wood. In the nineteenth century, as the processing of horn became more efficient and the buying of horn from farmers more regular, this material began to surpass all others, so that by mid-century only one Leominster combmaker (out of about twenty-five) was still using tortoiseshell.[21]

The manufacture of combs from horn required elaborate preparation of the raw material and very careful sawing and cutting. Horn, because it was a by-product of beef production, was not a very expensive commodity. Its use, however, did require careful initial selection, seasoning, cleaning, trimming, splitting, and pressing, processes that together took many days and considerable skill. Even then, the most skillful preparer of horn could not guarantee that his product would not split or crack under working. While methods for clarifying or staining horn were perfected in the early nineteenth century, they still allowed only a narrow range of colors or decorative effects.[22] The making of the comb itself necessitated shaping prepared plates of horn and planing the plates to assure an even thickness. Teeth were then either sawn in the blanks or cut by machines developed only in the first part of the nineteenth century. If the teeth were cut, it was possible to make two combs from one blank by "twinning," or cutting a zigzag in the middle of the blank and pulling the resulting pair of combs apart. A great deal of trimming, smoothing, buffing, and polishing then remained to produce a finished product.[23] During the nine-teenth century numerous machines were developed to mechanize many of these processes, but the problems arising from the variability and limita-tions of a natural material could not be dealt with by mechanization. In-deed, the use of a natural substance stood as a barrier to further use of machines.

In the course of the century a number of new comb materials were pro-posed, including glass, porcelain, papier-mâché, enameled steel, and hard rubber.[24] This last proved very useful, and in 1860 a large comb-making firm in West Newbury, Massachusetts, began using hard rubber. But the use of rubber required new machinery, and difficulties with sup-plies compounded problems, causing the manufacture there to be aban-doned.[25] The use of hard rubber for combs was important, but it never took hold in the traditional Massachusetts combmaking centers or in Oyonnax.

The American manufacture of combs from celluloid began with the establishment of the Celluloid Brush Company in 1874. This was one of the numerous companies set up in Newark for the production and sale of celluloid articles, but unlike a number of other manufactures, combmak-ing was not new to Newark. In the 1840s a prominent Newburyport combmaker moved his operations to the New Jersey city, and although his establishment later moved on, it attracted German immigrant comb-makers who carried on the industry in the city permanently. Despite the existence of combmaking in Newark, the celluloid makers early turned to Leominster for skilled craftsmen. There is, in fact, some evidence sug-gesting that Leominster combmakers were using celluloid in the mid-1870s.[26] Nonetheless, it was not until the 1890s that celluloid's real impact was felt in the traditional comb centers.

Celluloid in combmaking allowed for both easy manufacture and a quality product. In contrast to the quirky and inconsistent natural materials, celluloid could very easily be cut and rolled into sheets of the desired thickness and uniformity. It could be colored to look like horn, tortoiseshell, or ivory, or it could be given colors and decorative effects impossible with the natural substances. Celluloid produced a hard comb, but it could, in working, be softened as easily as horn and cut with even greater ease. It could be decorated by embossing, carving, stamping, or in a large number of other ways, most of them more easily effected and more surely done than was possible with horn or other traditional materials. It is therefore not surprising that the first makers of celluloid combs were successful. It was probably a combination of the competition represented by this success, pressures on the horn supply (not to mention tortoiseshell),[27] and the intrinsic advantages to be gained by working with the more tractable and versatile plastic that caused the traditional comb-makers to shift their attention and their craft to celluloid.

In the period between 1890 and 1910 the combmakers in the traditional centers of Leominster and Oyonnax, as well as elsewhere in America and Europe, shifted from the use of horn and other natural materials to that of celluloid. Not only was this one of the few important instances in which a traditional industry (one could almost say craft) replaced natural materials with celluloid on a large scale, but it also caused profound changes in the industrial life of the comb centers. In 1901 the Viscoloid Company of Leominster was formed to produce celluloid combs from material of its own manufacture. Within a few years it became an impor-tant general producer of celluloid and a fabricator of plastics products that included not only combs but also toys, brushes, hairpins, optical frames, and so forth.[28] In 1902 the Societé Oyonnaxienne was formed to supply the combmakers of Oyonnax with celluloid.[29] Two years later, the Establissements Convert was also producing celluloid in Oyonnax, and a little later the Societé Lyonnaise du Celluoid established production in the town.[30]

In Leominster the fabrication of plastic articles besides combs and of the machinery for working with plastics became the dominant industry of the town, eclipsing the narrower comb manufacture. An observer writing in 1909 noted the change that the town's industry had undergone. "For generations," he said, "Leominster has been known as the greatest pro-ducer of horn goods in the world, and to-day the same is true relative to its output of celluloid goods."[31] The Foster Grant Company was one of the firms established originally for making plastic combs, but taking advan-tage of the versatility of the material with which it was working, it became a prime example of the Leominster shift from combs to plastic articles in general. New plastics-forming machinery and new plastic materials enabled companies like Foster Grant to diversify and sometimes to create entire new markets for new products, such as the plastic sunglasses for which Foster Grant became so widely known.[32] And in one of the public squares of Oyonnax there still stands a floral monument to sunglasses, evidence of the identical pattern of diversification that took place in the French town.

These two instances illustrate that the shift in materials in some in-dustries can be so important as to change the entire economic and technological climate in which that industry operates, even when the product itself undergoes only minor changes in appearance and function. Leominster and Oyonnax became plastics-manufacturing centers, whereas before, they had been simply combmaking towns with long tradi-tions of concentration in that single industry.[33] The making of combs became just one of a variety of fabrications that were a part of a larger plastics industry. Industry was dominated by the large plastics manufacturers and the fabricators that could command the large amounts of capital called for by a diversified plastics manufacture. The links with remaining craft traditions were destroyed, and the material rather than the product dominated industrial life.

The Image of a New Material

With the increasing use of celluloid came increased public attention. Commentators on technical and economic matters began occasionally to refer to the new material in both the scientific and the popular press. Celluloid began to take on a reputation and an image, partly as a result of the efforts of its makers, but also as a result of the economic and social context in which its markets were found. The popular perception of a new technology is not static; it changes as the role and value of the technology changes. This perception is also not monolithic, for different segments of the community will react differently to the introduction and spread of a novelty. The significance of popular perceptions has not been ignored by historians of technology, for it is readily apparent in the case of such overwhelming engines of social change as the railroad, the factory system, or the automobile. For such technologies, the popular image may be complex, but the shape and expressions of it are not difficult to find. An innovation with more limited impact, such as celluloid, is also the source of perceptions and impressions, but these are frequently less obvious, so their changes and varieties are more difficult to chronicle. This difficulty does not, however, diminish their importance for understanding both the experience and the legacy of a new technology.

The dominant characteristic of celluloid in the eyes of most commentators was its use for imitation. The first general press notice of Hyatt's product was as "Gun Cotton Ivory."[34] An editorial in the *New York Times* for 16 September 1875 (p. 4) illustrated, in a tongue-in-cheek fashion, the extent to which celluloid was identified as simply imitation ivory:

> The recent explosion in Newark has made many people aware for the first time of the existence of celluloid. That pleasing compound, which presents itself to the ordinary eye in the guise of a white substance somewhat resembling ivory, is said to be composed of gun-cotton, camphor, and a number of other articles which even the most sanguine and visionary elephant would never dream of attempting to convert into ivory. Nevertheless, after the manufacturer of celluloid has subjected his gun-cotton to the action of camphor, and, say, laudanum, rhubarb, nitro-glycerine, and a few other medicinal and explosive substances, the result is an imitation of ivory

which is said to be regarded as a very good imitation by those persons who think that it closely resembles ivory.

A few months later a short notice of the Newark explosion in the *Journal of the Society of Arts* referred to celluloid as "a hard elastic substance, susceptible of high polish, and so closely resembling ivory as to deceive skilful experts by its appearance."[35] The confusion between celluloid and its popular ivory form was common in the first years of celluloid manufacture and was probably not unwelcome by the producers of the material, since it eased celluloid's introduction to consumers and allowed sellers to associate the material with a familiar and respected substance.

For the first twenty years that celluloid was on the market, the identification of the material as an imitation substance was paramount in its uses and in public descriptions of them. An article that appeared in the spring of 1879 in the *New York Evening Post* and subsequently in *Scientific American*, the *English Mechanic*, the *Journal of the Franklin Institute*, and *Iron Age* with only slight variations described the primary use of celluloid as the imitation of ivory.[36] Another such article, by W. H. Wahl, a well-known scientific journalist, originated in the *Journal of Industry* and later appeared in the *Journal of the Franklin Institute*, *Iron Age*, the *Popular Science Monthly*, and even, much shortened, in the *New York Times*.[37] Imitation tortoiseshell, amber, malachite, coral, and other decorative minerals were also seen as important applications. Even where celluloid was not used as a decorative imitation, it was a direct imitative substitution for a traditional material: as a substitute for porcelain in doll's heads, for parchment in drumheads, and for linen in collars and cuffs. Once celluloid began to be used as a substitute for other than luxury materials like ivory, functional considerations such as durability, ease of working, and so forth began to play a role in the selection of its applications.[38]

A characteristic of most descriptions of celluloid, in this period and thereafter, was a certain blandness or lack of enthusiasm. The substance was seen as useful and admirably versatile, but in no way as a wonder or even as a product of modern science. This restrained appreciation may seem strange to observers living in an age filled with the hyperbole of the miracles of modern chemistry, but it was celluloid's experience from the day Alexander Parkes displayed his wares among the "Vegetable Substances" at the 1862 London Exhibition. There is no evidence that the celluloid makers minded.

The typical image of celluloid was well illustrated by the display set up by the Celluloid Manufacturing Company at an exhibition of "novelties" sponsored by the Franklin Institute in Philadelphia in 1885. Among the articles displayed were

> brushes, combs, hand-mirrors, jewelry, cork-screws, card and soap-cases, powder boxes, pen-racks, paper-knives, thimbles, chessmen, checkers, shoe-hooks and horns, napkin-rings, glove-stretchers, parasol, umbrella and cane handles; mouthpieces for pipes, collars and cuffs, knife-handles for table cutlery, keys for pianos, organs and musical instruments and organ stops; martingale rings and harness trimmings, white and colored letters for signs, stereotype plates to print from, billiard and pool balls, trusses and surgical instruments, frames for eye-glasses, etc.; plates for false teeth, emery wheels, whip-handles, carriage mountings, corset-clasps, dress-steels, etc.; moldings for show-cases and decorated work, etc., etc.[39]

This constituted a very representative list of the articles made from celluloid in the mid-1880s. With very few exceptions, the objects included in this list are the same sort of small dry goods that dominated the market for celluloid from the beginning.

One of the outcomes of this Philadelphia exhibit was a report on celluloid made to the Franklin Institute by its Committee on Science and the Arts.[40] The committee recommended the awarding of a gold medal to the Celluloid Manufacturing Company for their product and lavished considerable praise on the material. The nature of that praise, however, indicated the limits of celluloid's attraction. The material was characterized as "a very valuable substitute for ivory" and "a very desirable substitute" for amber and vulcanite (hard rubber). To be sure, the variety of uses for celluloid was remarked upon, and it was said that "in each case it had positive advantages over the material it replaced," but, with one exception, effective imitation seemed to be celluloid's primary virtue.

The exception was the use of celluloid for stereotype plates, an outlet apparently being pushed by the Celluloid Manufacturing Company with some vigor. Perhaps the first mention of this use was a French suggestion that appeared in the *Journal of the Franklin Institute* in 1880.[41] One of the members of the Franklin Institute committee, Samuel P. Sadtler, emphasized the possible importance of the use of celluloid for stereotype plates in an article that appeared in *Scientific American* in January 1887.[42] According to Professor Sadtler, celluloid plates did not wear as fast as metal, they were easier to produce and to transport, and they performed as satisfactorily as any other material. While stereotyping with celluloid was practiced by a number of printers in the late nineteenth and early twentieth centuries, the plastic never replaced metal very widely.[43]

The attention given to the possibilities by Sadtler, however, was symptomatic of a general desire by the makers and promoters of celluloid for the material to break out of the narrow confines of toilet and novelty uses. The last sentence of Sadtler's article reflected this wish: "The rapid advances made in the application of this most interesting chemical product leave no room for doubt that it will play a very important part among the materials of construction in many manufacturing and technical processes in the future."[44] Celluloid never was to play such a role, but the boosters of the material clearly thought that the status of celluloid as an important material in its own right could be achieved only if it was adopted for important technical uses, rather than solely for small domestic articles.

Promotion and Promises: Collars and Cuffs

The search for special technical uses was not the only way in which celluloid manufacturers tried to identify and present the unique characteristics of their product. Even in the more mundane applications the special properties of celluloid were the focus of many advertising and sales campaigns. The lengths to which the manufacturers went in their efforts to depict the positive advantages of celluloid suggests the magnitude of the urge to make celluloid something more than a purely imitative material.

The best example of early celluloid products that were imitative and yet marketed on the basis of their special properties was celluloid "linen"— collars and cuffs. Few items were more dependent on their effective imitation of the real thing, and celluloid manufacturers continually sought better methods for making their products look like good linen. Some were made with linen layered between thin sheets of celluloid as a way of most effectively giving the product the feel of linen's weave. Processes were patented for forming and finishing celluloid collars and cuffs to give them the most convincing linenlike appearance. (J. W. Hyatt alone received eleven patents for collar and cuff manufacture.) Unquestionably, the most successful celluloid linen was that which did not look, feel, or smell like celluloid.

Yet the celluloid collar or cuff was definitely sold on the basis of the fact that it was *not* linen. A celluloid item usually cost roughly twice the price of linen, so it was obviously not marketed on the basis of inexpensive imitation (as were combs, for example), but on the basis of its superior properties. The superiority of celluloid lay in its resistance to wear and its ease of cleaning. The detachable linen collar and cuff had originally been devised earlier in the nineteenth century as a means for saving on shirt laundering, allowing collars and cuffs to be washed, starched, and

pressed after each wearing, while the shirt was worn several times between washings. This naturally appealed largely to members of the growing middle class, in both urban and rural areas. By the late nineteenth
century, however, detachable linen was a popular and acceptable fashion
for a broad spectrum of society. Celluloid linen sought to appeal to the
lower end of the linen market by offering still further savings in laundering. The celluloid collar and cuff did not wilt or fray in use and could be
washed by simply wiping off surface grime. Thus for the purchase of only
a couple of celluloid items, the wearer could dispense with as many as a
dozen pieces of linen and do away with the bother of laundering
altogether.

The efforts of the celluloid makers to promote the use of their product
as a linen substitute generated the most attractive and revealing of all
celluloid advertising—particularly in the form of trade cards (Figs. 4.1
through 4.4). Most of these simply commented on the waterproof
qualities of the new material, sometimes in charmingly indirect ways (as
in the series featuring the frog and elf or that with youngsters sporting
oversized linen) and sometimes a bit more explicitly, even if still with
tongue in cheek (as in the case of the natty suitor and the irate father).
The most striking to the modern eye, however, are those advertisements
touting celluloid's impact on the laundryman. The pandering to nativism
in celluloid's promise of "no more Chinese cheap labor" stands more as a
reflection of American mentality in the late nineteenth century than it
does of celluloid's true market appeal. Nonetheless, it illustrates the
lengths to which the material's promotors sought to exploit every avenue
open to them.

These lengths can be illustrated in a different way by the prose that was
sometimes found on the back of the advertising cards. On the reverse of
one could be read: "Celluloid being composed almost wholly of camphor,
imparts to these goods its great medicative qualities. Being worn around
the neck and pulse of wrists, they positively prevent and cure throat and
lung complaints and ward off contagion and Malaria."[45] Here was a
questionable attempt to turn the largely undesirable camphor odor of
celluloid into a saleable advantage.

Because of celluloid's high price vis-à-vis linen collars and cuffs, promoters had to appeal to customers on the basis of the product's special attributes. The difficulty of doing this was compounded by the failure of
celluloid to achieve any measure of fashionableness. A survey of several
volumes of four haberdashery journals dating from the early 1880s to the
1920s reveals numerous discussions of the fashion and trade in collars,
but not one mention of celluloid.[46] The fashion-consciousness of these
journals ranged from the very stylish *Haberdasher* to the more sports-

Figure 4.1. Many advertising cards for celluloid collars and cuffs were simply amusing reminders of the waterproof qualities of the product. Figures 4.1–4.4 courtesy of the Warshaw Collection of Business Americana, National Museum of American History, Smithsonian Institution.

Figure 4.2. Advertising cards sometimes tried to combine an appeal to practicality with the image of fashionableness — with questionable success.

Figures 4.3 and 4.4. The celluloid advertisers' exploitation of anti-Chinese sentiment was often quite explicit. The card above, in Figure 4.3, unfolded to reveal the full-size card below.

Figure 4.4. Further examples of nativist advertising in trade cards.

oriented *Clothiers' and Haberdashers' Weekly,* but it made little difference: celluloid was simply not a fashionable material.

Despite some evidence that the celluloid manufacturers considered collars and cuffs a very important part of their product line (see text at n. 12,
above),[47] celluloid linen represented no more than a small fraction of the
total market in collars and cuffs. One author in 1895 remarked on the
booming condition of the linen industry and then added that celluloid, "at
one time also employed, is now little used."[48] The *Census of Manufactures* for 1905 stated that almost 90 percent of the collars and cuffs in the
United States were manufactured in Troy, New York. Since there is no
indication of celluloid fabrication in Troy (the only important celluloid
collar and cuff producers being the Celluloid and Arlington companies),
this suggests that celluloid could not have accounted for more than 10 percent of the total volume of collars and cuffs, and probably constituted
much less.[49] The use of celluloid for collars and cuffs may have been one
of the most famous applications of the material, but it was not particularly important either economically or stylistically.

Celluloid and Fashion

The makers of celluloid had to confront problems of style and fashion in
promoting numerous articles. Spectacle frames were another area where
fashion was a major hindrance to widespread use of celluloid. One of the
Celluloid Manufacturing Company's earliest licenses was taken out by
the Spencer Optical Manufacturing Company, which intended to use the
material in making spectacle frames, lorgnettes, loupes, magnifiers, spectacle cases, holders, and wipers.[50] Frames were clearly the most important item in this list. Frame styles in the nineteenth century, however, did
not readily lend themselves to the use of celluloid. While frames made of
horn or shell had been made since the eighteenth century, metal was the
dominant material and seemed likely to remain so. An author writing in
1896 remarked on what was then the fashion in frames:

> The heavy framework of bone, horn and tortoiseshell, worn by our grand-
> fathers, are a contrast indeed to the dainty light setting of modern glasses,
> the aim of the good spectacle makers of today. A frame of the slightest fine
> steel, or the lightest of gold, compatible with the safe holding of the lens,
> makes the wearing of glasses much less irksome than they must formerly
> have been.[51]

Celluloid was not even mentioned in the history of spectacle frames in the
nineteenth century. Very cheap frames were made of hard rubber from
the 1850s, but their market derived solely from their low price. In 1908

the most popular materials for frames were reported to be metallic. It was only when tortoiseshell frames began to come into fashion about the time of the First World War that plastic started to make real inroads into the spectacle market.[52] Celluloid was most likely to be a follower, not a setter, of fashion.

Sometimes the manufacturers of celluloid directly confronted the problem of the fashionableness of their product. One very fashion-conscious class of products was that of toilet articles. While combs, brushes, mirrors, and other grooming aids had long been sold in fancy matched sets, after the turn of the century boxed sets of toiletware became one of the most important forms in which such articles were advertised and sold. These sets were made as moderately priced luxury items, appealing to much more than considerations of cost or practicality. The sales approaches for these articles reflected celluloid manufacturers' solutions to the problems of style and fashion.

The Celluloid Company developed an extensive line of toilet goods made from its best imitative forms of celluloid—"Ivaleur," "Amberleur," "Shelleur," and "Eboneur." Even after the First World War Ivaleur was the most important of these. A manual issued to Ivaleur salesmen in 1919 indicated how the company thought its product should be presented:

> Taking it for granted that the ideal toilet ware must answer all the requirements of utility and of durability, the all important quality is that of *artistic appeal.*
>
> To-day the skill and effort applied to the designing of IVALEUR Toilet requisites is comparable only to that employed in the manufacture of the highest class silverware and jewelry.
>
> Impress upon your customers the idea of ART in toilet ware, and assure them as you may with all truth, that in "IVALEUR," made only by The Celluloid Company, they will find the highest artistic achievement.
>
> In these days of far-reaching economies, many women, who have not already done so as a matter of good taste, will turn from the ostentatious silver toilet ware to that which is less expensive though really more beautiful. . . . Make your show pieces look more than their artistic value—make them look like priceless specimens of art which, owing to the wonders worked by modern chemistry and industry, made their production possible. Cater to your best trade—the other will naturally follow. Play up the word ART. Let it be the keynote of your selling argument.[53]

It was no coincidence that this was the sales pitch developed in the first years of what Russell Lynes called the era of "Corporate Taste."[54] This kind of selling was a good example of the new efforts of manufacturing enterprises not only to appeal to fashion, but to assert themselves in the defining and spreading of "good taste."

Contemporary observers were not oblivious to this development. One commentator writing in a toiletries trade journal suggested that while the plainer goods that the celluloid makers put out originally did sell and even achieved some popularity, they did not fill any real need. He then credited French manufacturers with the idea of producing finely designed imitation ivory articles from celluloid. This "French Ivory" was an instant success. The reason was significant:

> Did they supply a need? Indeed, yes. The need for something as a substitute for silver, exclusive enough to warrant its purchase by the richer class of trade, and meeting at the same time the growing demand of the day for a sanitary article. Such a brush did not tarnish; such a brush could be cleaned by the ordinary process of soap and water; moisture would not split or check it or dull its polish. It was white—the prevailing color of sanitary articles. Rich, solid, heavy and lasting! To top the scale the refinement of monogram in color to match the individual taste, placed it immediately in a class above the best article of silver or wood.[55]

The appeal to practicality was still there, but art and taste were the primary considerations. This appeal to fashion was so great that French designers may have been given the credit for the development of "French Ivory" simply because it made the material more stylish to appear to have come from the studios of Paris rather than from the factories of New Jersey. And of course the use of the French ending -eur for the Celluloid Company's product lines was another attempt to give celluloid products the aura of Paris fashion.

The concern for artistic image was apparent not only in the words of the manufacturers but also in the products themselves. Examples of the celluloid toilet goods sold by Du Pont in 1922 are pictured in Figure 4.5. The patterns, carrying names like "La Belle," "DuBarry," and "Mayflower," were adorned with various standard decorations that could be further enhanced by personal monograms, these being offered in a variety of colors and patterns. All of this was available in a number of basic color effects. Ivory remained, even through the twenties, the most important, but it was joined by tortoiseshell, amber, and pearl effects in white, gold, rose, and blue.[56] Despite the great extension of decoration and design in these objects, the imitative foundation of celluloid's appeal was still very evident. Indeed, as a material for small wares, celluloid never escaped its essentially imitative form.

The imitation of materials like ivory or shell in celluloid articles was not always directed towards replacement of these materials, but rather of more common substances. The references to silver and wood in the sales discussion quoted above are direct evidence of this. Substitution and im-

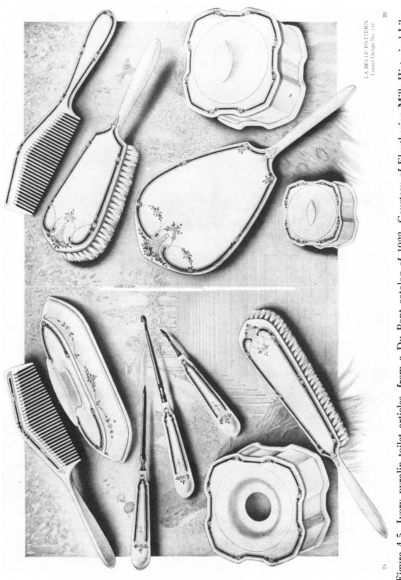

Figure 4.5. Ivory pyralin toilet articles, from a Du Pont catalog of 1922. Courtesy of Eleutherian Mills Historical Library.

itation were two separate functions. The following of imitative styles even when such styles were not related to the materials being replaced showed how bound the celluloid makers felt to the imitative role of their materials. It would have been easier to produce celluloid in the forms that are readily identified with the modern plastics—bright, uniform, solid colors intended to look like nothing other than plastic. Celluloid was rarely encountered in these forms. It began as imitation, and as a material for everyday objects, it remained imitation.

Sincerity and Imitation: The Plastic Dilemma

Every material used in art-manufacture is obviously restricted by the nature of its substance to certain conditions of form. Thus glass, which in a state of fusion can be blown or cut into a thousand fantastic shapes, admirably adapted for drinking-vessels, etc., would, from its brittleness, be utterly unfit for any constructive purpose in which even moderate strength was required. The texture of ordinary freestone, though capable of being treated with delicacy and refinement by the chisel of a practised sculptor, does not admit of that minute elaboration which we admire in wood-carving. In the manufacture of porcelain, and all kinds of ceramic wares, rotundity is the prominent type of form, while furniture and cabinet-work are generally quadrangular in their main outline, the general treatment in each case being suggested by the character and properties of the raw material. Whenever this condition is lost sight of, and the material is allowed to assume in design an appearance which is foreign to its own peculiar attributes, the result is inevitably inartistic and vulgar.

—Charles Eastlake, *Hints on Household Taste*

Charles Eastlake's *Hints on Household Taste* first appeared in America in 1872 and immediately became the fundamental word on "good taste."[57] Eastlake's basic criterion for good taste was sincerity. Therein lay the dilemma of the celluloid makers. How was a plastic material, whose most important virtue was its versatility of form and appearance, to be "sincere"? How could celluloid be designed in ways not "foreign to its own peculiar attributes"? It could not. The fact that celluloid emerged as a fabricative material at precisely the time that Eastlake's work was exerting its influence (and that influence lingered for decades) helps to explain some of the considerations of the celluloid manufacturers in choosing how they presented their products.

The theme running throughout the history of celluloid's application to the making of common articles was imitation. Despite the high value placed on sincerity by the tastemakers of the last quarter of the nineteenth century and the early twentieth century, imitation was the only important form that celluloid assumed. The imitation was usually very good. Celluloid ivory looked just like the real substance. Distinguishing celluloid tortoiseshell from genuine shell often required demonstrating the greater brittleness of the latter—and likewise with imitations of amber, horn, coral, or a variety of other materials. But celluloid was always imitation: it never was and never could be "sincere." Hence, the celluloid makers had to appeal to more prosaic middle-class values. Their articles were beautiful, durable, and inexpensive—not "ostentatious" like silver or fragile like real ivory or shell. Yet, by appealing to such values, by never being able to set their own standards of good taste, celluloid makers lost all chance of setting styles and fashions of their own. They locked themselves into the imitative stance that had seemed at first the only safe one to assume. It did not serve them badly, but it always circumscribed the form and the function of their material.

Following the patterns of production, fabrication, and selling established by the first celluloid producers in the 1870s, a viable celluloid industry emerged in the succeeding decades. Successful manufacturers and fabricators survived the competitive struggle with other plastics producers and with other materials. The experimentation and weeding out of the first two decades of the industry had succeeded in determining celluloid products that would sell to fruitful and stable markets. The products developed in the first years of the industry were refined in the ensuing decades, but their basic image and character changed little in the first fifty years of celluloid's widespread use. While appeals were consistently made to considerations of economy and practicality, imitation remained celluloid's primary virtue in most of its applications. While the imitative role was natural for the material when it was new, the persistence of that role throughout its history suggested the uneasy and ambiguous status of the first synthetic plastic. The first important function of this plastic was to look and behave like something it was not. This identification of plastics as "cheap imitation" is still with us. It is as much the reflection of the legacy of celluloid as it is of reality.

5

Culmination and Consequences

THE FUNCTIONS of celluloid were not wholly determined by the efforts of its makers. As the nineteenth century drew to a close and the twentieth began, the material played two very important roles, quite different from each other and from those found profitable by its producers. One of these was the realization of the hopes of celluloid's developers—the application of the material to a use for which it was uniquely suited and in which it displaced all rivals. This was the achievement of the inventors of celluloid film. The large-scale adoption of celluloid in photography revolutionized that medium, made another medium, cinematography, technically feasible for the first time, and gave celluloid its most significant breakaway from imitation. The widespread use of celluloid in photography, and in older areas, drew attention to the material's faults as well as to its uses. This was most clearly demonstrated by the concern over the substance's flammability. Hence came a search for substitutes for celluloid.

The second important but unexpected role played by celluloid was as a model for plastic materials—both of what such materials could be and of what they should not be. By both its virtues and its shortcomings, celluloid provided many of the central themes to be taken up by the seekers of new materials in the twentieth century. Could a material be made cheaper, harder, more durable, less flammable, more workable, more beautiful, or more versatile than celluloid? Such questions had to be answered to judge a new plastic meaningfully. As new plastics that met such criteria began to emerge and as styles and techniques changed, celluloid began to diminish in importance, but not before it had demonstrated the possibilities of an entire class of new substances.

Breakaway from Imitation: Celluloid and Photography

In all of the important uses hitherto dealt with, celluloid was judged and adopted on the basis of its ability to imitate effectively an older material.

90

This was true even where celluloid was valued for advantages which it possessed over traditional materials, as in waterproof collars and cuffs. The effort to find important technical or industrial applications for celluloid reflected the feeling that an outlet for which celluloid was uniquely suited was necessary if the material was to be of more than trivial importance. Such an outlet eventually was found—photography —and the joining of celluloid and photography was not only of profound importance for the developing medium, but it also had a great impact on the new material. Once celluloid had broken away from imitation, it could never again be looked upon as simply "artificial ivory."

Because of celluloid's kinship with collodion and the popularity of the collodion-based wet-plate process for photography in the decades after 1850, it might be imagined that the use of celluloid for photography was an obvious notion. But photographic collodion was used purely as the carrier for photosensitive chemicals, usually on a glass plate, and not as a support for the image itself. Hence it required some imagination to suggest the appropriate form in which celluloid could be used in photography. The first mention of the possibilities was Daniel Spill's 1870 paper before the London Photographic Society, noted in Chapter 3, above. Here he referred to his hope that he would someday be able to produce from xylonite "a flexible and structureless substitute for the glass negative supports."[1] This was at least more imaginative than the suggestion that appeared in the oft-reprinted *Evening Post* article of 1879 (see Chapter 4 at n. 36), where celluloid's identification with ivory was so strong that the one reference to photography was the substitution of celluloid in ivorytypes, that is, photographs printed on ivory or an ivory-like background.[2] Later references to celluloid as a photographic base returned to Spill's idea of substituting the material for glass plates, thus saving weight and avoiding breakage.[3] Other authors proposed using celluloid for lantern slides,[4] or as an all-purpose surface for any type of picture, photographic or not.[5] By the late 1880s the notion of using some form of celluloid in photography was no longer novel.

These early ideas about the use of celluloid as a photographic base were essentially as imitative as any of the older applications of the material. The great impact of celluloid upon photography and of photography upon celluloid was not to be the result of celluloid's replacing glass or some other material in a conventional camera. It stemmed instead from an entirely new concept of the photographic base—roll film. The idea of using flexible films as a surface on which to take photographs can be traced back to the early 1850s, and the concept of using such materials in rolls with several exposures, as opposed to simply sheets, can be found in a number of British photographic journals in the mid-1850s.[6] The first successfully manufactured roll film system was that of Leon Warneke, who began work in 1875. This system was rather expensive and not commercially successful, but it did serve as a model to those who followed. Warneke's film, like that of his predecessors, was a "stripping film"—a roll of paper coated on one side with sensitized gelatin or collodion or both and perhaps some other substance as well, which was processed and then stripped from the gelatin/collodion negative.[7] The stripping process and handling the unsupported negatives were very delicate operations, and roll films were not successful as long as they depended upon stripping.

The development of the ultimately successful roll film system was due to the efforts of a number of men, but it was popularly identified with only one, George Eastman. In the early 1880s Eastman was an important maker and dealer of photographic supplies (primarily dry plates—gelatin-coated plates, which by this time had largely replaced collodion plates) in Rochester, New York. In late 1883, Eastman and William H. Walker, another Rochester photographic outfitter, teamed together to try to devise a workable and commercially viable roll film system. The idea of a system should be emphasized, for success would require not only a good roll film, but also the means to produce such film with consistent quality in great quantity and a camera that would hold the film and reliably indicate how much film had been used at any given time. By the end of 1884, Eastman and Walker had devised and patented the elements of their system—a gelatin-on-paper stripping film, a process for producing it, and a film holder that was a marked improvement over previously designed roll holders.[8]

In 1885 Eastman and his backers began to market the new roll film and its holder. While the holder was admired for its ingenious construction, there were difficulties with the stripping film. At first, blistering of the film's coating made it unusable, so Eastman had to resort to making paper film rolls—gelatin-coated paper that was used without stripping—for his holders. The resulting negatives, however, were not transparent; thus they yielded fuzzy or grainy prints, to the dismay of most users. Even when an improved stripping film came to market, it turned out to be so difficult to produce and to use that it soon became obvious that it could not be the basis of Eastman's new system. This failure spurred Eastman to think even more boldly. He decided that if the market would not accept his new system, he would have to create a new market.[9] To do so, to take photography out of the hands of the technician and put it into the hands of the common citizen, Eastman had to develop a system more revolutionary than simply a new photographic base and a holder for it: he had to create an entirely new way of thinking about photography. In short, he had to create the Kodak.

"You press the button and we do the rest," epitomized the idea of the Kodak. By the middle of 1888 Eastman and his co-workers had developed and were ready to market a small, simple-to-operate, inexpensive camera, loaded with a one-hundred-exposure roll of Eastman's stripping film. After the amateur had completely exposed the film in his Kodak, he was to send the camera back to the Eastman factory, where the exposed film would be removed, processed, and printed, and the camera reloaded with another roll of film. The new camera was an immediate success and photography was never again the same.[10] Eastman was not satisfied with his stripping film, however, and even while he was introducing the Kodak, he began exploring the possibilities for a flexible, transparent film base. Celluloid was an obvious candidate. Eastman put a young chemist by the name of Henry Reichenbach to work on the problem of making celluloid suitable for film production. By early 1889 Eastman and Reichenbach filed applications for patents on their celluloid film and on machinery for making it.[11]

The development of a successful celluloid film required more than simply mechanisms for forming celluloid in the desired manner; it also required changes in the chemical composition of the material. Primarily, it involved the dilution of normal celluloid with a suitable solvent so that the material could be spread into very thin layers that would dry into stable, uniform films. The important solvent this time was amyl acetate, first discovered and patented as a celluloid solvent by the Celluloid Manufacturing Company's principal chemist, John H. Stevens, in 1882.[12] In the late 1880s this fragrant liquid was already being used to make a varnish from celluloid and was hence widely known as a celluloid solvent. Reichenbach's contribution was to devise the precise formulas and techniques necessary for making a uniform celluloid film suitable for photography.[13] Given the publicity that already surrounded the notion of a celluloid photographic base and the common knowledge of the amyl acetate solvent, it should not be surprising that Reichenbach was not the only person claiming the invention of a satisfactory celluloid film.

This is not the place to discuss the rancorous patent fight between Eastman and Reichenbach, on the one hand, and the Newark pastor, Hannibal Goodwin, on the other. Suffice it to note that Goodwin filed his first patent claim for a celluloid film in the summer of 1887, but sloppiness in the preparation of his application held up the issuance of the patent until 1898. Goodwin's patent did not differ markedly from Reichenbach's, except that it was more general. After extensive litigation, in 1913 the Eastman Kodak Company was finally found in infringement of the Goodwin patent. The flourishing company then paid the owners of the patent $5 million for the right to continue making celluloid film. The important point for our story is that the patent fight did not prevent Eastman Kodak from continuing to market celluloid film from the time of its first public sale in August 1889. The reception of the film was extraordinarily enthusiastic, and within a year Eastman had to expand his production facilities to meet the demand for the film and for the camera that used it.[14]

The use of celluloid for photographic film allowed the production of a photographic base that was sturdy, flexible, and capable of being produced with a consistently high quality. No other photographic film material combined these features. Dependence on a gelatin-paper stripping film would always have limited the use of the Kodak and of Eastman's film to photographers who were willing to send their camera and film to the Eastman company for unloading, processing, and reloading. Celluloid film, on the other hand, could be handled by anyone and processed by any knowledgeable amateur. While the initial success of the Kodak did not depend upon the use of celluloid film, the continuation and expansion of that success was in large part due to the perfection of Eastman's complete system of photography. The development of a dependable and versatile film base was a key achievement. Perhaps even more important for the history of celluloid, the use of the material for film depended upon a combination of transparency, flexibility, toughness, and uniformity that no other known substance possessed. Celluloid film imitated nothing. It substituted the almost ideal for the obviously imperfect.

As significant as was the contribution made by celluloid to still photography, it was even more fundamental in cinematography. Where celluloid added to photography a great new dimension of versatility and appeal, motion pictures as we know them would not have been possible without celluloid. The first projected motion pictures used glass discs, but this was obviously severely limiting. With the introduction of the first Eastman roll film, experimenters with motion pictures quickly began working with paper film, the stripping film being obviously too fragile for projection purposes. Paper film, however, did not possess the pure transparency needed for a good, clear projected image. About the time that Reichenbach and Eastman were beginning to produce a satisfactory celluloid film for still photography, a number of cinema experimenters, particularly William Friese-Green and E. J. Marey, turned to celluloid. At first, these experimenters used celluloid strips, made from ordinary celluloid blocks, but Reichenbach's transparent film was quickly substituted. It is impossible to say when the first celluloid roll film motion picture was made, but by the early 1890s numerous individuals were working with celluloid, designing film, cameras, and projectors that took advantage of the strong, flexible, transparent material. In 1895 a number of inventors in America and in France began showing motion pictures to paying audiences. Celluloid was firmly established as the only satisfactory material for the new medium.[15]

With the general adoption of celluloid in photography and, especially, cinematography, the technological and economic significance of the material attained a new and quite different status. Finally an outlet for which celluloid was uniquely suitable had been found and exploited. Indeed, only a few years into the twentieth century, photography without celluloid became unimaginable. The dependence of motion pictures upon the new material was so great and so obvious that the medium began to take on the name of the material. Hence references to the heyday of the movies as "the celluloid age," and to film stars as "celluloid personalities."[16] By the late 1920s the amount of celluloid motion picture film was spoken of in terms of "trillions of miles,"[17] and it was quite likely that still and motion photography accounted for the largest segment of the celluloid market, at least until the development of safety (acetate) film in the 1930s. Equally important, however, was the fact that photography freed celluloid from the confines of imitation and substitution by giving it a technological niche all its own.

One can detect a yearning on the part of celluloid's makers for such a niche from the very beginning of the material's commercial history. Celluloid's final achievement as an "indispensable" material by the end of the nineteenth century was the consummation of the efforts to make a useful pyroxylin plastic and to find a stable, mature market for it. On the other hand, it is significant that the celluloid companies had almost no hand in this consummation. Despite the fact that it was a Celluloid Manufacturing Company chemist that discovered the usefulness of amyl acetate as a solvent, the exploitation of celluloid and amyl acetate in the making of a useful film base was due to the work of Reichenbach and Goodwin, neither of whom were associated with the celluloid manufacturers. The celluloid makers also reaped little benefit from photographic applications of celluloid. Eastman Kodak, which accounted for most of the film market, produced most of its own materials. Eastman's rivals, such as the Blair Camera Company, did purchase celluloid from the established plastics producers, but these companies constituted a relatively minor segment of the total market.[18] Similarly, the celluloid makers had nothing to do with the adoption of celluloid for cinematography. Eastman quickly captured the market for cinema film, thus leaving the plastics producers shut out of that lucrative line as well.[19] The development of celluloid film was a remarkable example of the conjunction of two emerging technologies. With the application of celluloid to photography, the new material finally entered the realm of "high technology," where its properties acquired new technical importance. The celluloid industry, however, was foreign to this realm, and was hence left behind.

The Unavoidable Problem: Flammability

Celluloid, whether used in photographic film or in common household or personal articles, did not tend to attract much attention to its physical or chemical properties. While photographic applications did make use of celluloid's unique combination of characteristics, the focus of such applications was clearly on the photography or cinematography for which celluloid was simply part of the technical base. Even when attention was directed towards film itself, professional and general concern was usually for the characteristics and quality of the emulsion and not the film base. Celluloid's application in toiletries and other small wares was generally so imitative that it was the quality of the imitation and of the accompanying design that was of interest to manufacturers and consumers alike. The physical characteristics of the material were not particularly important so long as it possessed the expected hardness and durability. There was one property of celluloid, however, that was of special interest to all its makers and users—its flammability. With the expanding use of celluloid, concern over the safety of the material became widespread.

The *New York Times* editorial entitled "Explosive Teeth" that appeared in 1875 was a portent of widespread and long-lasting concern over the safety of celluloid.[20] Indeed, this concern can be traced back to parts of the patents issued to Alexander Parkes in the 1850s in which he suggested materials that could be added to parkesine to make it safer.[21] The explosion and fire in the Celluloid Manufacturing Company's works in Newark in September 1875 was only the first of numerous disasters that plagued celluloid manufacturers in this country and abroad. In the space of only 36 years, the celluloid factory on Newark's Ferry Street was the scene of 39 fires and explosions, resulting in at least 9 deaths and 39 injuries.[22] Mention has already been made of the fires that hampered celluloid production in Germany (see above, Chapter 4). The production and fabrication of celluloid was either banned or placed under strict controls in many jurisdictions on account of the hazards.[23] The natural dangers of celluloid production—to be expected in an activity involving primarily nitrocellulose and camphor and their combination under heat and pressure—had considerable effect on the manner in which celluloid products were viewed.

To its credit, the *New York Times* editorial "Explosive Teeth" tried to dispel the notion that celluloid itself, as opposed to its components, was explosive. A few days after this editorial appeared, the *Times* reported the conclusions of a coroner's jury in Newark that "celluloid as placed on sale in its varied forms of utility or ornament, is a product entirely distinct from its component parts, and with none of the peculiar qualities of either, except that of combustibility. Aside from its destructibility by fire, which is not more than that of sealing-wax, celluloid is a safe article in the common uses of daily life."[24] Unfortunately, a few years later there appeared on the *Times* editorial page another humorous piece, entitled "Presents," that told the story of a lover who gave his sweetheart celluloid dress-items, only to see her blown to bits when he lit his cigar while sitting by her.[25] Most stories about celluloid concerned the real danger of fire rather than the imaginary one of explosion, but the public did not always see this distinction.

A scrapbook of clippings and pamphlets put together by an official of the Celluloid Manufacturing Company is filled with indications that combatting the dangerous reputation of celluloid was a major concern of the celluloid manufacturers.[26] The Newark company's confrontation with the problem began in its first years, as is shown by the *Proceedings* of the Lyceum of Natural History in the City of New York. In a meeting on 10 October 1870, a Professor Seely warned stridently of the dangers of operating with guncotton and camphor at high temperatures. To counteract the fears conjured up by such denunciations, the celluloid manufacturers recruited their own professors. Over the years eminent consulting chemists like Charles F. Chandler of Columbia University were hired to argue the safety of celluloid.[27] Nevertheless, as a Celluloid Manufacturing Company chemist said many years later, the company's 1875 fire created a long-lasting distrust of their operations among the people of Newark, a distrust that was directed not only towards celluloid's manufacture but also towards its use.[28]

Concern over celluloid's safety led to numerous experiments to test the material. An April 1892 issue of *Scientific American* noted a case in which the celluloid buttons on a dress had been ignited merely because the wearer was near a bright fire.[29] The article continued by describing experiments showing that pieces of celluloid burst into flame more readily than match heads. This piece was followed a few weeks later by another describing tests that suggested that the danger of spontaneous ignition was really not so great.[30] Both of these articles were taken from British reports. British concern over celluloid's safety was evident for a long time. In 1912 the home secretary appointed a "celluloid committee" to "inquire and report as to the precautions necessary in the use of celluloid in manufacture and the handling and storage of celluloid and celluloid articles." The extensive report of the committee, issued in 1913, reviewed the composition and application of celluloid and the dangers associated with its manufacture and use. Its recommendations were largely for greater care in labeling celluloid items and greater caution in their use, as well as greater safety measures for establishments where celluloid was present in quantity, such as cinemas.[31] One of the conclusions of the committee was that celluloid had become a permanent fixture of industry:

> Failing the production on a large scale of non-inflammable substitutes of an equal commercial value, there is no reason to believe that the use of celluloid will decrease in the near future. On the contrary, the increasing scarcity of certain natural substances, such as tortoise-shell, ivory, and amber, necessitates an increasing use of celluloid as a substitute.[32]

Thus, the fire hazard from celluloid was always a source of worry, but it did not deter either manufacturers or consumers from using and accepting the material even for cigar holders and children's toys.

Substituting for the Substitute

Flammability was not the only widely recognized fault or limitation of celluloid. The material had to be protected from exposure to heat at all times, even when the danger of fire was not present. At about the boiling point of water celluloid softened considerably and became subject to chemical decomposition. This instability, sometimes evident even at room temperatures, meant that even in photography celluloid was not the perfect plastic. By its virtues celluloid demonstrated the possible uses for plastic materials. By its faults, celluloid spurred on a search for substitutes, for newer and better plastics. As the nineteenth century drew to a close, the search for new materials began to expand beyond attempts to imitate natural substances. New plastics were described as substitutes for celluloid itself. Celluloid provided the model for what a modern plastic material must accomplish. This was perhaps celluloid's most significant role.

Just as earlier efforts at producing substitute materials were marked by numerous strange and unlikely recipes, so was this one. A short item that appeared in the *Milwaukee Sentinel* sometime toward the end of the century remarked that "the many uses and inflammable character of celluloid have led to an active search for substitutes." It then went on to describe a material made of "a mixture of cellulose, asbestos, and the organic matter contained in oyster shells."[33] There were also numerous patents taken out for "improved" celluloids, often including such ingredients as turpentine or gelatin.[34] Many of these "improvements" were directed towards correcting particular faults or imparting special qualities to celluloid. They did not make important changes in the material (except perhaps for the worse) and were not important.

More significantly, among the celluloid substitutes developed in the period from 1890 to 1910 were important new plastics, including the casein plastics, viscose, and the first synthetic resins.[35] Numerous experiments in the nineteenth century tried to produce a plastic material using milk solids as a base, and in the 1890s some useful materials were developed. An article on artificial ivory that appeared in 1891 included an amusing reference to one of the first casein plastics and to its relation to celluloid:

> Those who have encountered certain 'hard' cheeses of rural manufacture will appreciate the degree of tenacity, resistance to attrition, or, in fact, any mechanical agency, which casein can attain under suitable conditions, and be quite open to conviction as to its powers as a wear-resisting material. It is perhaps to be regretted that a composition so essentially robust should be saddled with a name like 'lactite,' suggestive of some farinaceous abomination designed for the euthanasia of the rising generation. It is curious and instructive to note that it is put forward as a substitute for celluloid, a substitute for a substitute in fact. Altogether its inventor has fallen into an error not common in his class, viz., that of over-modesty, verging on self-depreciation.[36]

The most useful casein plastic was a German invention produced by reacting dried casein with formaldehyde. By the early 1920s, this "galalith" (from the Greek, meaning "milk-stone") was the single most popular material for the fabrication of buttons. The town of Schmölln, in Thuringia, underwent the same sort of transformation in its button manufacture that Leominster and Oyonnax had experienced with combs.[37]

Another material inspired in part at least by the search for a celluloid substitute was cellulose xanthate, or viscose. In 1892 two English chemists, Charles F. Cross and Edward J. Bevan, discovered that cellulose that had been treated with caustic soda would, upon reacting with carbon disulphide, produce a very viscous liquid which they dubbed "viscose."[38] The finished "viscose" or "viscoid" was cellulose xanthate that had been "ripened" (by treatment with an alkali solution or simply by standing) until it had reverted into almost pure cellulose. Viscose is usually associated with rayon, or regenerated cellulose fibers, and Cross and Bevan were primarily seeking an artificial silk. Nevertheless, the substance was used as a plastic and as a possible alternative to celluloid in some products, such as knife handles or hollow articles.[39] Viscose was never popular for such articles, and its only economic importance was in the production of synthetic fibers.

A cellulose derivative that was much more important as a substitute for celluloid was cellulose acetate. The first successful acetylization of cellulose was achieved by Paul Schützenberger in 1869. Despite the efforts of numerous chemists over the next decades, the acetyl derivatives of cellulose remained purely of laboratory interest until the early twentieth century, when the Dreyfus brothers and others succeeded in solving numerous production problems. Cellulose acetate was also widely used as a fiber (known as "celanese"), but it quickly gained a reputation as a nonflammable substitute for celluloid. Its high price, however, prevented it from replacing the older material very widely until the 1930s.[40]

Organic Compounds and Aniline Dyes:
The Synthetic Legacy

Two extremely important ideas converged in the early twentieth century to produce celluloid's successors. One of these was the notion of a generally useful plastic material. This concept originated with the exploitation of the natural plastics in the early and middle nineteenth century and found its most important manifestation in celluloid itself. The other fundamental idea was that of the chemical synthesis of materials, including not only the production of natural substances by chemical means, but also the creation of new materials not found in nature. The knowledge and appreciation of chemical synthesis also emerged in the middle of the nineteenth century, developing along narrow though fruitful lines throughout the last half of the century. The most important achievements in chemical synthesis were those of the organic chemists. Their work produced not only an enormous variety of new substances, but also methods that could be widely applied in the analysis of materials and in the creation of yet more new substances. Beyond accomplishments in the laboratory, however, they sought out the application of their discoveries and methods to the production of useful products and the creation of entire new industries. By the beginning of the twentieth century there existed a well-known and wonderfully successful model of what could be accomplished by the marriage of creative chemistry and industrial organization.

In 1828 Friedrich Wöhler, a German chemist then teaching in Berlin, synthesized urea by reacting lead cyanate with ammonium hydroxide. Urea hitherto had been found only in animal wastes and was generally considered a true "organic" material, a substance produced only by natural living processes. The synthesis of urea was perhaps the single most important event in establishing that there were no theoretical barriers to what the chemist could put together in the laboratory, given the proper simple substances and the right conditions for their combination.[41] The many possibilities of organic synthesis continued to be explored as the nineteenth century progressed. These included not only the synthesis of complex organic materials from inorganic substances, but also the production of numerous organic compounds that were not to be found in nature. In the 1850s the synthesis of organic substances became the subject of systematic study by chemists like Marcellin Berthelot, whose *Chimie organique fondée sur la synthèse* (1860) set forth general methods for the synthesis of a wide variety of organic compounds. Such synthesis was of considerable importance in the elucidation of the principles of organic structure.[42]

The practical possibilities of organic synthesis were not lost on its proponents, however. The work of Justus Liebig and his laboratory at the University of Giessen and of later institutions established on Liebig's model, such as the Royal College of Chemistry in London, demonstrated the usefulness of organic analysis in agriculture and industry. The technological potential of organic synthesis was not fully revealed until 1856, however, when a young student at the Royal College, William Henry Perkin, discovered the first aniline dye. This dye, aniline purple or *mauve*, as the French named it, was the product of Perkin's effort to synthesize quinine from coal tar derivatives. The brilliant purple product of his experiments was able to color silk easily and cotton with the help of mordants. By the end of 1857 the firm of Perkin and Sons was manufacturing and marketing the first successful synthetic dye. After some initial resistance from British dyers, aniline purple met with considerable (though short-lived) commercial success. Beyond that, however, it spurred the development of other chemical dyes from coal tar products (especially aniline, toluidine, and quinoline). The first important aniline dye after mauve was fuchsine, or magenta, developed by the French in 1858. It was soon followed by aniline yellow, aniline blue, and imperial purple, among many other less successful colors. In the London Exhibition of 1862, twenty-nine European companies exhibited aniline dyes. With extraordinary speed, synthetic dye manufacture became a basic chemical industry.[43]

A number of circumstances made the synthetic dye industry a dramatic example of the possible benefits of applying chemical synthesis to industry. The first of these was the relative simplicity of the most important chemical transformations. Once Perkin had demonstrated the possibilities presented by fairly simple reactions with aniline, it was not a difficult matter for a large number of chemists, amateur and professional, to experiment with the enormous variety of possible reactions involving aniline and other coal tar chemicals. Such haphazard experimentation produced mostly worthless products, but a few genuinely useful ones were also discovered, reaping rich rewards for the lucky chemists and spurring many others to still further dabbling. The importance of synthetic dyes was enhanced by the raw material from which they were derived. Few chemical transformations could have been more striking than the derivation of a multitude of rich, bright colors from the unattractive and even offensive residue of coal distillation. Even more important than the drama of such a transformation were the economics. To use the by-product of coke and coal gas for the manufacture of fine chemicals was to use chemistry to turn almost worthless substances into universally valued ones.

Coal tar dyes also had the advantage of ready and easily expandable markets. Textile manufacturers did not have to make great adjustments in their ways of doing things to use the new dyes. In many cases the technical superiority of the synthetic dyes was so evident as to allow the dyes to sell themselves. If technical differences were persuasive, often the economic advantages of the new substances over the natural dyes were overwhelming. The synthesis of alizarin, the active agent of the most im-portant natural red dye, was the best example of this, ruining the centuries-old madder industry barely a decade after the initial manufac-ture of synthetic alizarin in 1869. Far from simply being superior to natural dyes, however, the coal tar products often produced colors im-possible with traditional dyes. Perkin's mauve was the first example, and dozens followed in the next few decades. Because the dye industry was in-timately linked to fashion-conscious textile and clothing markets, the de-mand for new colors was almost inexhaustible. This gave the synthetic dye manufacturers a uniquely powerful spur towards constant experimen-tation and innovation, making the industry the first one heavily reliant on continuous research and development.

With the exhaustion of the possibilities presented by simple reactions, the dependence of the synthetic dye industry upon the methods of syn-thesis developed by organic chemists became complete. One of the most important implications of this was the rise and eventual domination of the German dye industry, owing to the vast superiority of German chemical education over that available in Britain and France. Another conse-quence was the complete integration of advanced organic chemistry into the workings of a major industry. The manipulation of molecules and the creation of multitudes of new compounds became one of the central tasks of the dye manufacturers. In Germany this led to the creation of a substantial research apparatus contained both within the laboratories of the industry itself and in the universities, where men like August Wilhelm Hofmann and Adolf von Baeyer made crucial contributions to the development of new compounds. So fruitful was the German research establishment it produced not only dyes but also pharmaceuticals, per-fumes, and flavorings.[44] There could have been no better demonstration of the potential of the scientifically enlightened manipulation of organic molecules. By the beginning of the twentieth century there existed both the capability and the willingness to apply chemical knowledge to the creation of new substances.

Bakelite: Chemistry and Serendipity

This was a far different background from that existing in the 1860s when celluloid was developed. The importance of the differences can be appreciated best by studying the invention of Bakelite.

Bakelite was the first of the artificial resins, the most important substitutes for celluloid. After its commercial introduction in 1909, Bakelite was rapidly adopted for a wide variety of important uses and hence quickly assumed major commercial and technical importance. Beyond that, however, its success pointed the search for new materials into fruitful new directions. Bakelite was the first useful synthetic polymer. As such, its symbolic significance rivaled its commercial importance. Experience with celluloid contributed greatly to the widespread recognition of the usefulness of Bakelite. The forty-year history of celluloid's development and application prior to 1909 prepared the technical and business world and the public for ready acceptance of a new, versatile, cheap plastic material, one that differed markedly from celluloid and yet was clearly akin.

Bakelite's discoverer and namesake was Leo Hendrik Baekeland, a Belgian-born American chemist who made his first fortune by inventing a high-quality, nonfading, easily handled photographic paper that would take images using artificial light. This "Velox" paper was difficult to perfect, and its final success showed Baekeland to be an enormously skilled chemist. Besides requiring considerable chemical sophistication, the success of Velox also required entrepreneurial persistence and commercial acumen. The new paper was not readily accepted by professional photographers, the principal buyers of photographic supplies in the 1890s, because it required techniques substantially different from the traditional ones. Hence Baekeland was forced to direct his appeal to amateurs, who, less set in their ways, more readily appreciated the greater convenience and the higher quality of the new paper. By 1899 the superior qualities of Velox had earned widespread recognition, and Eastman Kodak bought the formula from Baekeland for $750,000. Baekeland had not only demonstrated his chemical and business skills, but he was also a wealthy man.[45]

With his money Baekeland provided his family with the comforts of life and himself with a laboratory and an assistant. In this laboratory Baekeland tinkered and dabbled. He involved himself in numerous projects, some of them pursued to great lengths and others only superficially.

A look at his personal diaries (which he began in April 1907) and at some of his laboratory notebooks conveys the image of a man fascinated by the possibilities of chemistry, but not especially concerned about any one project. He became a consultant to a company established to produce caustic soda and chlorine by electrolysis, and this occupied much of his time from 1904 through 1907. His diaries began less than three months before the invention of Bakelite, and yet they tell of work in his laboratory on making soybeans more palatable, utilizing waste bisulphite liquor for disinfecting wood, and developing an artificial shellac. While often describing his experiments in terms of specific practical problems, Baekeland clearly saw himself as a scientist, pursuing his research in systematic fashion, observing and noting all interesting phenomena. If his experiments yielded practical results, so much the better—Baekeland was a man who appreciated the application of science above all things—but his efforts were not directed or defined by any single need or commercial opportunity.

Investigation of the reactions between phenol and aldehydes began in 1872 with the work of Adolf von Baeyer, the German chemist whose most famous achievement was the practical synthesis of indigo. In 1891 another German organic chemist, Werner Kleeberg, reported on experiments with phenol and formaldehyde. Kleeberg described the product of the simple combination of these substances as a hard amorphous mass, infusible and insoluble. Such an intractable substance was of little interest or use to the chemist, and Kleeberg's investigations stopped there.[46] Other workers, however, took up the study of phenol-formaldehyde reactions, often with applications in mind. In Baekeland's first public announcement of his invention, in a lecture before a section of the American Chemical Society in 1909, he described many of the experiments that had preceded his. A number of these were clearly directed towards producing a plastic molding compound. For example, in 1902 Adolf Luft attempted to modify Kleeberg's composition by adding solvents like glycerine or camphor to the reacting mass before it hardened. Baekeland's observation was: "The whole process of Luft looks clearly like an attempt to make a plastic similar to celluloid and to prepare it and to use it as the latter. The similarity becomes greater by the use of camphor and the same solvents as in the celluloid process."[47] Baekeland then described Luft's product as "relatively brittle, very much less tough and flexible than celluloid." Certainly the connection between the search for a celluloid substitute and that for a tractable product of phenol and formaldehyde was well established before Baekeland entered the field.

Other investigators of phenol-formaldehyde reactions were interested in soluble products, particularly in possibilities for shellac substitutes. Baekeland's own assistant, Nathaniel Thurlow, apparently had an independent interest in this problem. He and Baekeland, following the work of others, pursued this line of research for a number of years, attempting to perfect a product they called Novolak.[48] The most important variables in the experiments of Baekeland and Thurlow, as in those of numerous other researchers working in the 1900s, were the condensing agents and the temperature and pressure conditions under which the phenol-formaldehyde reaction was run. The fusibility and the solubility of the reaction's products differed greatly depending on these factors. In the course of his research, Baekeland apparently became aware of the influence of a number of the variables with which he was working. For instance, if acid condensing agents were used, the products tended to be more fusible and soluble; if bases were added, then the reaction tended to yield infusible and insoluble products. The importance of this lay in determining just what Baekeland was trying to produce by his experiments.

Baekeland's diary for the spring of 1907 contained very little mention of Novolak, the soluble phenol-formaldehyde product that he and Thurlow were trying to market as a shellac substitute (with meager success). But on 18 June 1907, while Thurlow was absent, Baekeland began a new laboratory notebook, writing on the first page, "I intend to report systematically different tests relative to my process for hardening woods with condensation products." He then described tests made on various pieces of wood to which had been applied, in different ways, a half-and-half mixture of phenol and formaldehyde.[49] Here he was trying to harden the wood by impregnating it, rather than by coating it, as with a shellac-like product. Baekeland's notebook entry for 19 June reported a significant observation that shifted his attention away from problems of wood hardening. The entry deserves to be quoted in full:

All these tests were conducted in concentrated horizontal digester and the apparatus was reasonably tight. Yet the surface of the blocks of wood does not feel hard although a small part of gum that has oozed out is very hard.

I began to think that the formaldehyde evaporates before it can act and that the proper way would be to impregnate with the viscous liquid which is obtained by boiling $CH_2O + C_6H_5OH$ together without a catalytic agent. In order to determine in how far this is possible I have heated in sealed tubes a portion of this liquid so as to determine whether there is a further separation of H_2O or whether this is simply a phenomenon of drying, and if the liquid is simply a solution of the hard gum in excess of phenol, then by simple open air evaporation I shall be able to accomplish hardening while I shall not succeed in closed sealed tubes.

I have also heated an open tube rammed with a mixture of asbestos fiber and liquid.

Also a sealed tube rammed with mixture of asbestos fiber and liquid.

Everything heated 4 hours at 140° C–150° C.[50]

The results of this work must have been quite wonderful, for the change in tone in the notebook entries was startling. The entry for 20 June 1907 began unhesitatingly, "In order to facilitate matters I shall designate in the future the different products by a special name." Baekeland then went on to describe four substances, A, B, C, and D. This last was "insoluble in all solvents, does not soften. I call it," Baekeland went on to say, "Bakalite [sic] and is obtained by heating A or B or C in closed vessels."[51] That Baekeland should instantly bestow this product with a commercial name is remarkable evidence that he recognized what he had found. The notebook description of the result of the last experiment outlined for the previous day was more explicit:

Asbestos + A in sealed tube. I found tube broken perhaps in irregular expansion but the reaction seems to have been satisfactory because the resulting stick was very hard and below where there was some unmixed liquid A there was an end [?] of solidified matter yellowish and hard and entirely similar to the product obtained by simply heating A alone in sealed tube. This looks promising and it will be worth while to determine in how far this mass which I will call D is able to make moulded materials either alone or in conjunction with other solid materials as for instance asbestos, casein, zinc oxid [sic], starch, different inorganic powders and lamp black and thus make a substitute for celluloid and for hard rubber.[52]

Elsewhere Baekeland referred to his hard, infusible solid as an "ivory like mass."[53] Leo Baekeland was not looking for a celluloid substitute, but he knew instantly when he had one.

Confirmation of Baekeland's ready recognition of the importance of his discovery can be found in a diary entry. He put down just one entry for 18–21 June 1907, in which he said, "I consider these days very successful work which has put me on the track of several new and interesting products which may have a wide application as plastics and varnishes. Have applied for a patent for a substance which I shall call Bakalite."[54] The reference to Bakelite's (Baekeland changed his spelling before announcing his patent) utility for "plastics" would not have been possible had there not already arisen a general notion about what "plastics" were. The source of this notion, more than anything else, was celluloid.

Bakelite was very different from celluloid. It would not soften on heating, it was not flammable, it was much more brittle, and it could be mixed with other materials much more easily. Nevertheless, the material was clearly akin to celluloid, primarily because it could be molded. In his public introduction of Bakelite before the New York section of the American Chemical Society on 5 February 1909, Baekeland made constant reference to celluloid when describing Bakelite's applications. He also made indirect references:

> It [Bakelite] makes excellent billiard balls of which the elasticity is very close to that of ivory, in short it can be used for similar purposes like knobs, buttons, knife handles, for which plastics are generally used. But its use for such fancy articles has not much appealed to my efforts as long as there are so many more important applications for engineering purposes.[55]

Just as celluloid's makers sought out the technical utility of their product, so did Baekeland, with much quicker success.

By 1912 the Albany Billiard Ball Company, John Wesley Hyatt's original enterprise, had adopted Bakelite as the ultimate satisfactory answer to the billiard ball problem.[56] Baekeland's invention possessed a versatility and ease of working far surpassing that of celluloid, and to boot, it was cheaper. One of Baekeland's key achievements was his recognition of how to utilize the chemical characteristics of his material. He continued to explain how to work with his product in terms of A, B, and C just as he had in his first notebook outline (he dropped the D, apparently concluding that it was insufficiently different from C). The liquid A could be used to impregnate materials, to coat materials, or for molding. It would then be heated for the proper length of time in a closed vessel (which he named a "Bakelizer") to produce the Bakelite product. Also possible, however, was the use of B, which was solid and yet fusible. B could be ground up into a powder, put into a mold, and then heated in a "Bakelizer" to produce a Bakelite product much more quickly than was possible by using A directly.[57] This was to be of great significance in the application of Bakelite in industrial molding, where the large number of castings that had to be made from a few expensive molds made the speed of molding a critical factor. Baekeland's recognition of such realities contributed markedly to the great speed with which Bakelite was adopted by makers of electrical insulators and other technical necessities.

The importance of Bakelite lay not only in its competition with celluloid (and other substances) as a cheap and versatile material, but also in its meaning for the future. Just as celluloid had inspired many chemists and would-be inventors to try their hand at making useful materials by relatively simple transformations of natural substances, Bakelite once again expanded the universe of possible materials. Its creation showed that giant molecules themselves could be manufactured by the clever chemist who persisted in seeking the right conditions for desired reactions. Perkin and the other pioneers of the synthetic dyes had demonstrated how the manipulation of molecules could produce myriads of fine chemicals. Rubber and celluloid had shown how useful materials could be made from natural polymers, large molecules made up of chains of simple organic units. Now Bakelite showed how men need not be limited to natural polymers, but could construct their own, imparting to the molecule those properties important to a particular application.

Many in the early twentieth century were aware of how special the achievement of Baekeland was and of how it had extended the already marvelous accomplishments of synthetic chemistry. A 1924 book, *The Story of Bakelite*, presented this striking picture of the chemist to the rescue:

> But it was in wood smoke and coal smoke, pouring up chimneys the world over, that [the Chemist] found the new treasures of earth, marvels which earth had never known—colors to shame the sunset, medicines for every ill, explosives to blow whole cities to pieces, perfumes surpassing Araby, sweets that have made Hymettus merely a figure of speech, and now a super-resin, Bakelite, answer of the Chemist to the call for a new rein on Electricity, the tricky, but titanic force that pulls the apple-cart of the human race.[58]

The invention of Bakelite marked the turning of the search for new materials away from a preoccupation with imitation towards a more direct concern for function. Materials were to be created, not to copy nature, but to rearrange nature in new and imaginative ways.

The Pioneer Fades Away

As the first synthetic polymer, Bakelite, more than any other material, established the pattern for the development of plastics in the twentieth century. The most important plastics of the twentieth century have been the man-made polymers: the thermosetting resins (urea-formaldehyde and others in addition to Bakelite), the polyvinyls, the acrylics, artificial rubbers, polystyrene, nylon, polyethylene, and countless others. This does not mean that the natural polymers disappeared from the scene. Indeed, the exploitation of cellulose expanded considerably beyond the cellulose nitrate and cellulose acetate materials to include plastics based on cellulose acetate butyrate, cellulose acetate proprianate, methyl and ethyl cellulose, and other modifications of the cellulose molecule. In addition, new forms of cellulose plastics were developed, the most notable being cellophane, which was introduced into the United States in 1924. In the twentieth century the search for the perfect plastic—the universal substitute and imitation—was abandoned. A function for every plastic and a plastic for every function became the new goal.[59] The very idea of a plastic carried with it the image of endless variety as well as infinite versatility.

The search for a celluloid substitute was successful. The replacement of celluloid, however, was not immediate. Sales of celluloid continued to rise until the mid-1920s.[60] Its uses continued to expand, reaching into such areas as flexible automobile windows and faddish green eyeshades. As late as 1938, a British government committee reported that "at the present time there is no other plastic material that possesses all the desirable properties of celluloid."[61] With the continuing proliferation of plastics this situation changed rapidly. When, in 1949, the factory on Newark's Ferry Street ceased manufacturing celluloid after 77 years, its product line had been reduced to collars and cuffs, still in demand in Texas, Oklahoma and parts of South America, and dice, the composition of which gamblers were reluctant to see tampered with.[62] Indeed, almost the only uses for which celluloid is still sought after today are those in which it has established a standard that can be duplicated only with great difficulty. It is ironic, in light of celluloid's experience competing with ivory billiard balls, that the best example of this is in table tennis balls.[63]

The fate of the celluloid manufacturers in the twentieth century reflected the fate of their product. In 1915 the Arlington Company was purchased by E. I. du Pont de Nemours, who continued to produce pyralin for many years. Du Pont acquired the Viscoloid Company of Leominster in 1925 and went on to become one of the major producers and innovators of plastics in the world. In 1938 the Fiberloid Company, having moved from Newbury to Springfield, Massachusetts, was purchased by Monsanto and became the foundation of that company's plastics manufacture. Finally, the Celluloid Company, having been partially absorbed by the Celanese Corporation in 1927, was merged completely into the larger company in 1941. The disappearance of the celluloid companies was due to their close identification with a single, old-fashioned product in a market quickly becoming inundated with a bewildering variety of new materials. Some of the companies began making cellulose acetate plastics in their last years, but this was not enough to allow for effective competition against large chemical companies able to produce and sell large numbers of the newer plastics. The old companies, having secured their markets at the beginning of the century, never developed the research and development apparatus that produced important innovations. Having fostered the idea of plastics, celluloid and its makers were largely engulfed and lost in the full growth of that idea in the twentieth century.

Conclusion

IN TERMS of quantity, celluloid cannot be said to have been an extremely important material in nineteenth-century America. Consumption never exceeded 500 tons a year until after 1905.[1] (In contrast, the consumption of rubber in the United States in 1900 was about 15,000 tons.)[2] The only use of celluloid that became dependent upon the material was photography, and while celluloid's contributions to popular photography and to cinematography were immense, they had hardly begun before researchers commenced efforts to find a substitute that did not have celluloid's flammability or tendencies to decompose under certain conditions. Celluloid did transform certain industries, such as comb-making, and hence certain industrial centers. This kind of impact should not be depreciated, but it was a very common thing in the nineteenth century. Indeed, from the eighteenth-century industrialization of Manchester to the Space Age transformation of Houston or Silicon Valley, such changes of industries and places have been a part of industrialization and modernization. Measured by the scale in which such things happened in the late nineteenth century, the changes that overtook Leominster and Oyonnax and even Newark were not large, except within a purely local framework. While celluloid had, by 1890, become an economically viable and technically useful material, widely accepted for many products and even demanded for some, it must be judged a rather small part of the productive and consumptive life of Europe and America.

Where, then, does the historical importance of celluloid lie? It is only in hindsight that celluloid can be recognized as the first artificial plastic. Whereas the importance of Bakelite as the first man-made polymer was quickly and widely acknowledged, the uniqueness and importance of celluloid as the first plastic produced by the chemical transformation of a natural material was seldom, if ever, remarked upon. Unlike, for example, William Henry Perkin's mauve, celluloid did not create an entirely

110

new concept of the possibilities of chemical creation. The invention of celluloid did not immediately suggest new vistas for the enterprising chemist, at least not in the way of the work of Perkin and Baekeland.

The significance of celluloid was not in its industrial or economic impact or in its chemical novelty, but rather in its role in the expansion of man's material capabilities, an expansion that was only beginning in the second half of the nineteenth century but that has become one of the most important technological and cultural outgrowths of industrial society. By the time celluloid was perfected, the widespread use of the natural plastics had publicized the possibilities and uses of plastic materials. While materials with properties similar to those of celluloid (though never quite the same) were common at the time celluloid was introduced, they were all simply mixtures or minor modifications of natural substances, of natural products that possessed some plastic properties in their original states. Celluloid, on the other hand, was produced from an omnipresent fibrous material changed by the action of very common acids and then made tractable by the addition of a crystallized resin. None of the original ingredients of celluloid suggested at all a hard, transparent, moldable product. If the manner of celluloid's invention broke no new ground, the substance still demonstrated that human fabrication was not limited to traditional materials.

The extent to which man could transcend the old boundaries which defined the materials with which he had to work was one of the great lessons of the nineteenth century. Not only celluloid, but also the new natural plastics, the new forms of iron and steel, and the new metals such as aluminum were evidence of a dramatic liberation from the restraints posed by the limited number of available materials in times past. The greatest significance of the history of celluloid lies in the light which it sheds on this liberation. In its development numerous problems central to the invention and exploitation of new materials were confronted with special clarity. The motivations for producing new substances are well illustrated by those given for developing celluloid. The problems of determining how a new material is to be used and successfully marketed were explicit features of its history. That history, therefore, suggests not only broader questions in the history of materials but also some key aspects of the dynamics of technological change.

The idea of a plastic made from nitrocellulose did not spring full-grown like Minerva from the imaginative head of a nineteenth-century chemist. It was suggested by dried collodion, which in turn was a natural result of attempts to exploit the curious properties of nitrated cellulose. These attempts, in turn, can only be attributed to the curiosity and perception of chemists like Schönbein. Celluloid was therefore, in part, the product of speculative chemistry. It was really much more than that, however. The efforts of men like Alexander Parkes and Daniel Spill to make solidified collodion into a useful substance were driven by the belief that a new and versatile plastic material was needed.

What it was needed for was another question. Parkes was attracted simply by the notion of a new substance—a substance that would be useful in the arts in ways different from rubber or gutta percha or ivory or wood. The idea of a new material, especially a new material that could be colored and molded, was a very real motivation for a man like Parkes. He spent his entire life working with materials, both metals and nonmetals. He combined the skills and experimental outlook of the Victorian metallurgical engineer with the aesthetic concerns of the traditional craftsman. Despite the abortive attempts to market it as a cheap substitute, parkesine was, to its creator at least, primarily to be valued for its artistic capabilities.

John Wesley Hyatt, on the other hand, had other notions of what was needed. Leo Baekeland's description of celluloid as but a "big parenthesis" in Hyatt's search for the perfect billiard ball was to some extent accurate. The aesthetic potential of his invention was not one of Hyatt's primary concerns. To him, a new material was needed largely because some older ones were becoming too expensive. If a satisfactory billiard ball could be made from a composition that cost only a fraction of what ivory cost, then such a billiard ball should be made. If the rubber monopoly was making hard rubber dental plates more expensive than dentists or their patients thought reasonable, then a substitute for hard rubber plates should be introduced. This attitude could hardly be called exceptional, especially in nineteenth-century America, and in a sense Hyatt's efforts should be classed with the innumerable attempts to produce "factitious" and "imitation" materials out of every sort of ingredient imaginable to replace almost any natural product of value. Hyatt was different because he succeeded.

Indeed, celluloid was different because it succeeded. Its success did not come easily, and the difficulties experienced in applying and marketing celluloid are the most revealing aspects of its history. The makers of celluloid, like many other inventors in the nineteenth century, had to confront directly the problem of what to do with their invention. This problem is perhaps the most intriguing element in the history of the new materials that were first exploited in the last century. Once a machine or vehicle or instrument is perfected, it is usually quite clear what purposes it can serve, at least initially. This was not true in the case of new materials like celluloid. The difficulties of the British developers of parkesine and xylonite were the most dramatic illustrations of this problem, but even the experiences of the eventually successful Americans were illuminating.

The eventual domination of imitation as the mode for marketing celluloid showed both the potential and the limitations of a new material. That celluloid could be made to look like a wide variety of other, much more valuable substances was one of its most remarkable properties. The exploitation of that property was the key to celluloid's successful marketing. Yet, imitation also circumscribed celluloid's potential and image as a popular material. Imitation, by its very nature, suggested inferiority. The first artificial plastic was for a long time economically viable only as an imitative, and hence "cheap," material. This established the identity between the "artificial" and the "imitative" and between "plastics" and "cheapness" which is still a part of popular wisdom.

That the imitative mode inhibited celluloid's assumption of any importance as a fashionable material was widely recognized. That it similarly made it almost impossible for celluloid to dominate any of the markets in which it found a role was an obvious and irritating fact to the promoters of the material. On the one hand, this conservative, imitative image allowed celluloid to find acceptance without trying to displace more established materials. And yet, it was clear that the material would thus always be at the mercy of fashions that it could itself influence very little. Furthermore, the future of celluloid would never be very secure without some important application in which it was more than a cheap substitute. This problem of the identification and securing of markets was the most pressing aspect of the development of new materials in the nineteenth century. Indeed, all new technologies had to confront this dilemma, and the responses of the makers of celluloid reflected generally on how nineteenth-century technologies established their own viability.

The displacement of traditional materials in key industries was the most obvious solution open to celluloid. That the material was able to do so in the comb industry, to some extent at least, showed that, given the right circumstances, this approach could succeed. Even in combs and toilet goods, however, celluloid makers felt compelled to follow traditional lines of fashion, imitating the designs and effects of traditional materials. If celluloid was to establish an identity and importance of its own, so its makers clearly felt, it would have to assume some special technical importance, become identified so closely with an advanced technology that technology and material would be inseparable. The eventual success of celluloid in revolutionizing photography and cinematography was the final justification for this thinking. In photography celluloid was no longer "artificial," "imitative," or even "unnatural."

Despite celluloid's impact on photography and its eventual acceptance in a few industries, its ultimate historical importance was in its replacement. As the nineteenth century drew to a close, the number of useful new plastics steadily increased. The most important model for these new materials was celluloid. By the end of the first decade of the new century, the first totally synthetic material, Bakelite, had been invented and launched as a successful commercial substance. This invention, herald of the modern mastery of material synthesis, was the first fruit of the conjunction of two nineteenth century ideas—that of organic synthesis and that of plastics. Celluloid was clearly the most important exemplar of the latter idea. Even without making a great economic impact or displacing traditional materials to a large extent, celluloid firmly established the versatile, moldable, colorful plastic as an integral part of the world of material possibilities. This was celluloid's greatest achievement. The extent to which this had been accomplished could not be recognized until the more modern and even more useful plastics of the twentieth century had begun to replace it. That replacement resulted in the end of celluloid's useful economic role. It also signified, however, the permanence of celluloid's essential technical idea.

Celluloid has long lost its economic or technical importance. It is now a figure of speech more than anything else, referring to movies or to cheap plastic sheets, themselves almost certainly not made of the material. That celluloid should remain part of the language while practically disappearing as a material is a reflection of the fact that the ideas represented by celluloid were and are of greater importance than the technology itself. Some of these ideas were integral with the technology. That celluloid should represent a plastic material synthesized from nonplastic substances was in the nature of the invention. For this reason the invention itself was significant, given the great role of synthetic plastics in the twentieth century. Others of the ideas represented by celluloid sprang from the application of the material. The dominance of imitation so strongly influenced the image of celluloid that it and all subsequent plastics have carried with them the stigma of artificiality. These ideas and perceptions remain significant features of modern technology. The importance of understanding the origins of these ideas in the history of celluloid lies not so much in the ideas themselves as the recognition of the complexity and power of the ideological dimensions of technology.

Reference Matter

Notes

Chapter 1: The Invention of Celluloid

1 Joseph Bersch, *Cellulose, Cellulose Products, and Artificial Rubber*, trans. W. T. Brannt (Philadelphia: Henry Carey Baird & Co., 1904), pp. 161–74 passim; Williams Haynes, *Cellulose, the Chemical That Grows* (New York: Doubleday & Co., 1953), p. 58.

2 *Dictionary of Scientific Biography*, s.v. "Braconnot," "Pelouze," and "Schön- bein"; Carl Marx, "With the Pioneers, I: Schönbein, Discoverer of Cellulose Nitrate," *Plastics* 2 (January 1926): 9–10, 30–32; Edward C. Worden, *Nitrocellulose Industry*, 2 vols. (New York: D. Van Nostrand, 1911), 1:21–22.

3 Between 1852 and 1916 British patents were numbered on an annual basis; hence, the year of issue is necessary for identification of the patent. In this work, British patents will be cited as here, with number and the year of issue.

4 Marx, "Pioneers, I," p. 30; Worden, *Nitrocellulose*, 1:21–22.

5 Worden, *Nitrocellulose*, 1:22–23, 2:899–900.

6 Worden, *Nitrocellulose*, 2:815.

7 Ibid., 2:828; Robert Taft, *Photography and the American Scene* (New York: Macmillan, 1938; reprint ed., New York: Dover Publications, 1964), pp. 118–19.

8 *The Letters of Faraday and Schönbein, 1836–1862*, ed. Georg W. A. Kahlbaum and Francis V. Darbishire (Basel and London: Williams & Norgate, 1899), pp. 151–52.

9 Ibid., p. 153.

10 Schönbein to Faraday, 18 March 1846, ibid., p. 155.

11 Ibid., pp. 154–55n.

12 Marx, "Pioneers, I," p. 31.

13 "Death of Mr. Alexander Parkes," *Engineering* 50 (25 July 1890): 111; Morris Kaufman, *The First Century of Plastics* (London: The Plastics Institute, 1963), p. 17.

14 Parkes made a significant contribution to rubber manufacture by his develop- ment of "cold vulcanization" (British Patent 1,147 of 1846). S. D. Sutton, "Rubber-Dipped Goods," in *History of the Rubber Industry*, ed. P. Schidrowitz and T. R. Dawson (Cambridge: W. Heffer & Sons, 1952), p. 303.

15 Alexander Parkes, testimony in Spill v. Celluloid Manufacturing Company, 2 Fed. Rep. 707 (Circuit Court, Southern District of New York, 1880), depositions in "Old Equity Case Files 1846–1877," Legal Records Division, Record Group 21, National Archives, Suitland, Maryland, Question and Answer 3X–10X.

16 Alexander Parkes, "On the Properties of Parkesine and Its Application to the Arts and Manufactures," *Journal of the Society of Arts* 14 (22 December 1865): 81.

17 Ibid.

18 Ibid., p. 82.

19 Ibid., p. 83.

20 Spill v. Celluloid Mfg. Co., 2 Fed. Rep. 708.

21 Spill v. Celluloid Mfg. Co., 21 Fed. Rep. 631 (1884).

22 Parkes, in Spill v. Celluloid Mfg. Co., Answer 24X.

23 Ibid., Question and Answer 83X–84X; see also Question and Answer 15–16.

24 This is the conclusion reached by Kaufman, *First Century*, p. 24.

25 Parkes's patents on parkesine and related materials were British patents 1,123 and 1,125 of 1856; 2,675 of 1864; 1,313, 2,733, and 3,163 of 1865; 1,564, 1,592, and 2,709 of 1866; 865 and 1,695 of 1867; and 1,366 and 1,614 of 1868.

26 Parkes, in Spill v. Celluloid Mfg. Co., Question and Answer 17–19 and 38.

27 Kaufman, *First Century*, p. 24.

28 Parkes, "Properties of Parkesine," p. 82.

29 Worden, *Nitrocellulose*, 2:570–71n.

30 A lively exchange between two prominent American chemists, Robert C. Schüpphaus (who had been associated with Spill's American ventures) and Charles F. Chandler (who had been a consultant for the successful American entrepreneurs) appeared in the *Journal of Industrial and Engineering Chemistry* 6 (May 1914): 440 and 6 (July 1914): 601–2.

31 The following information on the life and work of Daniel Spill is taken largely from Kaufman, *First Century*, pp. 28–32.

32 Ibid., p. 29; see also testimony of Parkes and of Daniel Spill in Spill v. Celluloid Mfg. Co.

33 Kaufman cites British patents 2,666 of 1867; 3,984 of 1868; 3,102 of 1869; 180, 787, and 1,626 of 1870; and 1,739 of 1875. Kaufman, *First Century*, p. 31. Additional patents are listed by Worden, *Nitrocellulose*, 2:571.

34 Daniel Spill, "On Xylonite, a Material Applicable to Photographic Purposes," *British Journal of Photography* 17 (23 December 1870): 603.

35 Daniel Spill, *appellant*, v. The Celluloid Manufacturing Company, U.S. Supreme Court, Appellate Case Files, No. 12305, Record Group 267, National Archives, Washington, D.C., pp. 17–18.

36 Worden, *Nitrocellulose*, 2:782–83. A list of the more than 1,200 American and British patents related to pyroxylin plastics can be found in *Nitrocellulose*, 2:773–92.

37 Ibid., pp. 574–75.

38 U.S. Patent 65,267 (28 May 1867), p. 1.

39 Spill v. Celluloid Mfg. Co. (Supreme Court), pp. 17–18; Worden, *Nitrocellulose*, 2:773.

40 Most of the biographical material on Hyatt comes from the following sources: Worden, *Nitrocellulose*, 2:576–79; Worden, *Technology of Cellulose Esters*, 2 vols. (Easton, Pa.: Eschenbach Printing Co., 1921), 1:2665; Kaufman, *First Century*, pp. 33–35; Charles F. Chandler, "Presentation Address," *Journal of Industrial and Engineering Chemistry* 6 (February 1914): 156–58; John W. Hyatt, "Address of Acceptance," *Journal of Industrial and Engineering Chemistry* 6 (February 1914): 158–61; P. W. Bishop, "John Wesley Hyatt and the Discovery of Celluloid," *Plastics World*, October 1968, pp. 30–38; and J. Harry DuBois, *Plastics History U.S.A.* (Boston: Cahners Books, 1972), chap. 2.

41 Worden alone seems to have appreciated the significance of this. Worden, *Cellulose Esters*, 1:2665n.

42 Hyatt, "Address of Acceptance," p. 158.

43 Ibid., p. 159. Chandler, "Presentation Address," p. 156, claimed Hyatt was not familiar with the earlier use of camphor.

44 Kaufman, *First Century*, p. 36, pointed out the irony of this.

45 Hyatt, "Address of Acceptance," p. 159.

46 Ibid., p. 160.

47 Carl Marx, "The Rise of the First Great Plastic Industry," *Plastics* 4 (December 1928): 670–71.

48 Worden pointed out how special this experience was: "Whereas in the usual development of an industry, the first methods and machinery are gradually replaced by others more productive or inexpensive, until often in a few years the industry has been so completely revolutionized in its methods and commercial demands that the original devices and manipulations are discarded as obsolete . . . pyroxylin plastic manufacture forms a notable exception to this apparently well-established experience, for the devices and refinements patented by Hyatt and others many years ago, stand to-day with but unimportant refinements the best examples of plastics practice and are used in essentially their originally described form." *Nitrocellulose*, 2:583n.

49 This description of celluloid manufacture is taken largely from Worden, *Nitrocellulose*, 2:582–614; other sources include the Celluloid Company, *Celluloid: How Celluloid Is Made* (Newark, N.J.: The Celluloid Company, n.d.); René Dhommée, "Fabrication du Celluloid," *La Revue Technique* 26 (10 May 1905): 372–73.

50 L. F. Haber, *The Chemical Industry, 1900–1930* (Oxford: Oxford University Press, 1971), p. 150.

51 The most complete standard treatment is in Worden, *Nitrocellulose*, chap. 14.

52 See Worden's comprehensive list of celluloid patents, *Nitrocellulose*, 2:773–81.

Chapter 2: Celluloid in Its Material Context

1 T. R. Dawson, "Chronology of Rubber History," in *History of the Rubber Industry*, ed. P. Schidrowitz and T. R. Dawson (Cambridge: W. Heffer & Sons,

1952), pp. xii–xiii; Williams Haynes, *This Chemical Age: The Miracle of Man-Made Materials* (New York: Alfred A. Knopf, 1942), pp. 173–77.

2 R. W. Parris, "Ebonite," in Schidrowitz and Dawson *History of the Rubber Industry*, pp. 296–301; Charles Goodyear, *Gum-elastic and its Varieties . . .*, 2 vols. (New Haven: for the author, 1855), vol. 2 passim.

3 Parris, "Ebonite," pp. 298–301.

4 T. Seeligmann et al., *Indiarubber and Gutta Percha*, trans. (from the French) J. G. McIntosh (London: Scott, Greenwood & Co., 1903), p. 278.

5 Ibid., p. 279; Eugene F. A. Obach, "Gutta Percha" (Cantor Lectures), *Journal of the Society of Arts* 46 (1897–98): 97–114, 117–33, 137–64, and 169–97.

6 Otto Neustatter, "A Lost Art in the Field of Plastics: Papier-Mâché . . .," *Plastics* 3 (May 1927): 206; *Encyclopaedia Brittanica*, 11th ed., s.v. "Papier-mâché."

7 Floyd Rinhart and Marion Rinhart, *American Miniature Case Art* (South Brunswick, N.J.: A.S. Barnes & Co., 1969), pp. 29–31.

8 Ibid., pp. 32–33.

9 Robert Angus, "Whatever Happened to Pure Virgin Vinyl? Why Records are Black," *Forecast!* February 1975, p. 60.

10 V. C. Rockhill, "Looking Back," *Plastics* 3 (June 1927): 300.

11 Alexander Parkes, testimony in Spill v. Celluloid Manufacturing Company, 2 Fed. Rep. 707 (Circuit Court, Southern District of New York, 1880), depositions in "Old Equity Case Files, 1846–1877," Legal Records Division, Record Group 21, National Archives, Suitland, Maryland, Question and Answer 80X–81X.

12 Edward C. Worden, *Nitrocellulose Industry*, 2 vols. (New York: D. Van Nostrand, 1911), 2:682.

13 "Gun Cotton Ivory," *J. Soc. Arts*, 19 (3 March 1871): 300.

14 Leo H. Baekeland, "The Invention of Celluloid," *Journal of Industrial and Engineering Chemistry* 6 (February 1914): 90.

15 Richard Owen, "The Ivory and Teeth of Commerce," *J. Soc. Arts* 5 (19 December 1856): 73.

16 "The Ivory Trade," *J. Soc. Arts* 12 (5 February 1864): 190.

17 *New York Times*, 7 July 1867, p. 3.

18 Heinr. Ad. Mayer, *Ivory* (Hamburg, 1876), p. 11.

19 "Artificial Ivory," *J. Soc. Arts* 14 (1 December 1865): 45.

20 "An Artificial Ivory," *J. Soc. Arts* 14 (16 November 1866): 782–83.

21 William B. Dick, *Dick's Encyclopedia of Practical Receipts and Processes*, ed. Leicester Handsfield and Harriet Handsfield (New York: Funk & Wagnalls, 1975; reprinted from unspecified 1870s ed.), p. 200.

22 "Scarcity of Ivory," *J. Soc. Arts* 30 (9 June 1882): 814.

23 P. L. Simmonds, "Our Supplies of Ivory," *J. Soc. Arts* 30 (29 September 1882): 1018–19.

24 Heinr. Ad. Meyer, *Ivory*, pp. 23–31.

25 "The Ivory Trade," *J. Soc. Arts* 47 (25 November 1898): 39.

26 George F. Kunz, *Ivory and the Elephant in Art, in Archaeology, and in Science* (Garden City, N.Y.: Doubleday, Page & Co., 1916), p. 253.

27 Worden, *Nitrocellulose*, 2:682n.

28 Alfred Maskell, "Ivory in Commerce and in the Arts" (Cantor Lectures), *J. Soc. Arts* 54 (2 November 1906): 1136. This, according to figures given by Kunz, *Ivory and the Elephant*, p. 254, was an exaggeration.

29 "The Ivory Trade" (1864), p. 190; Michael Phelan, *The Game of Billiards*, 4th ed. (New York: D. Appleton & Co., 1859), p. 34.

30 Kunz, *Ivory and the Elephant*, pp. 243–47.

31 Phelan, *Billiards*, p. 34.

32 John W. Hyatt, "Address of Acceptance" (of the Perkin Medal), *Journal of Industrial and Engineering Chemistry* 6 (February 1914): 158–59.

33 E.g., "How Celluloid Billiard Balls Are Manufactured," *Scientific American* 48 (19 May 1883): 306.

34 Albany Billiard Ball Company, *Hyatt Billiard and Pool Balls* (Albany, 1899).

35 "Artificial Ivory," *The Engineer* 72 (16 October 1891): 311–12; George Wright & Company, *Eburnea, the Synthetic Ivory* (London, 1890s?).

36 James H. Prothero, *Prosthetic Dentistry* (Chicago: Medico-Dental Publ. Co., 1916), p. 554.

37 *The Dental Cosmos* 13 (1871): unnumbered advertising page.

38 Ibid.

39 Ibid. 15 (1873): unnumbered advertising page.

40 "The Perkins-Hyatt (Celluloid) Base," *British Journal of Dental Science* 14 (1871): 364–68.

41 *The Dental Cosmos* 15 (1873): unnumbered advertising page.

42 See also Celluloid Manufacturing Company, *Celluloid as a Base for Artificial Teeth* (New York: Celluloid Mfg. Co., 1878).

43 Worden, *Nitrocellulose*, 2:720.

44 Jean Delorme and Pierre Laroux, *Les Conquêtes des matières plastiques en médecine et en chirurgie* (Casablanca: Les Editions Amphora, 1950) p. 88.

45 Prothero, *Prosthetic Dentistry*, p. 439.

Chapter 3: The Search for Markets

Portions of this chapter appeared in altered form in "Parkesine and Celluloid: The Failure and Success of the First Modern Plastic," *History of Technology*, vol. 4, (London: Mansell, 1979), pp. 45–62.

1 Alexander Parkes, testimony in Spill v. Celluloid Manufacturing Company, 2 Fed. Rep. 707 (Circuit Court, Southern District of New York, 1880), depositions in "Old Equity Case Files, 1846–1877," Legal Records Division, Record Group 21, National Archives, Suitland, Maryland, Question and Answer 13X. Elsewhere Parkes suggested that his experiments began as early as 1849; see Question and Answer 11X and 16X.

2 Ibid., Question and Answer 12X, 14X, and 15X.

3 London International Exhibition of 1862, *The Illustrated Catalogue of the Industrial Department: British Division* (London: for Her Majesty's Commissioners, 1862?), p. 103.

4 *Cassell's Illustrated Family Paper Exhibitor* (London: Cassell, Petter & Galpin, 1862), pp. viii–ix.

5 Exhibit, "London Exhibition 1862," in Spill v. Celluloid Mfg. Co.; this is reprinted in Morris Kaufman, *The First Century of Plastics* (London: The Plastics Institute, 1963), p. 22.

6 Parkes, Spill v. Celluloid Mfg. Co., Answer 49X.

7 Henry J. Parkes, Spill v. Celluloid Mfg. Co., Answers 4 and 11; see also the testimony of Walter Sellwood, Answer 12.

8 *Cassell's Illustrated*, p. 43. This same paragraph appears with only slight variations in John Timbs, *The International Exhibition* (London: Lockwood & Co., 1863), p. 90.

9 Exhibit, "The Parkesine Company, Ltd.," in Spill v. Celluloid Mfg. Co.

10 Ibid.

11 On the reception of the Atlantic cable, see Vary T. Coates and Bernard Finn, *A Retrospective Technology Assessment: Submarine Telegraphy—The Transatlantic Cable of 1866* (San Francisco: San Francisco Press, 1979), chap. 4.

12 Alexander Parkes, Spill v. Celluloid Mfg. Co., Answer 220X.

13 Alexander Parkes, "On the Properties of Parkesine and Its Application to the Arts and Manufactures," *Journal of the Society of Arts* 14 (22 December 1865): 82; see also Parkes's testimony cited above, Spill v. Celluloid Mfg. Co., Answer 15X.

14 Alexander Parkes, *Brief Account of the Invention and Manufacture of Parkesine* (Birmingham: Corns & Bartleet, 1867), p. 3. This work appears as Exhibit, "Parkes' Pamphlet," in Spill v. Celluloid Mfg. Co.

15 Exhibit, "Liquidation," in Spill v. Celluloid Mfg. Co.

16 Alexander Parkes, Spill v. Celluloid Mfg. Co., Question and Answer 231X.

17 Daniel Spill, testimony in Daniel Spill, *appellant*, v. The Celluloid Manufacturing Company, U.S. Supreme Court, Appellate Case Files, No. 12305, Record Group 267, National Archives, Washington, D.C., p. 234.

18 Daniel Spill, Jr., testimony in Spill v. Celluloid Mfg. Co., Question and Answer 215X.

19 Kaufman, *First Century*, p. 29.

20 Cited in Robert C. Schupphaus, "The Invention of Celluloid," *Journal of Industrial and Engineering Chemistry* 6 (May 1914): 440.

21 Daniel Spill, "On Xylonite, a Material Applicable to Photographic Purposes," *British Journal of Photography* 17 (23 December 1870): 604.

22 Kaufman, *First Century*, p. 30.

23 "Master's Report," Spill v. Celluloid Mfg. Co. (Supreme Court), pp. 1326–27.

24 Exhibit A, ibid., pp. 1047–50.

25 Exhibit B, ibid., pp. 1061–62.

26 "Inventory, June 30, 1887: Cellonite Manufacturing Company," Arlington Company Accounts, Records of E. I. du Pont de Nemours & Co., Series II, Eleutherian Mills Historical Library, Greenville, Wilmington, Del.

27 U.S. Department of Commerce, Bureau of the Census, *Biennial Census of Manufactures, 1921* (Washington, D.C.: U.S. Government Printing Office, 1924), p. 717.

28 Carl Marx, "The Rise of the First Great Plastic Industry," *Plastics* 4 (December 1928): 671, 684.

29 Records of R. G. Dun & Co., *New Jersey*, 22: 280, and 23: 144, 391, 422; *New York*, 245; 2140–41, and 390: 2453. Archives and Manuscripts Department, Baker Library, Harvard University Graduate School of Business Administration, Boston, Mass.

30 R. G. Dun & Co., *The Mercantile Reference Book*, vol. 88 (March 1890), rating listed under "New Jersey, Essex County, Newark."

31 Marx, "The First Great Plastic Industry," pp. 671, 684.

32 "Master's Report," Spill v. Celluloid Mfg. Co. (Supreme Court), p. 979.

33 Ibid., p. 1002.

34 William F. Ford, *The Industrial Interests of Newark, N.J.* (New York: Van Arsdale and Co., 1874), pp. 22–23.

35 Ibid., pp. 21–22.

36 Great Britain, Home Department, *Report of the Departmental Committee on the Use of Celluloid in the Manufacture of Toys, Fancy Goods, etc.* (London: H.M.S.O., 1938), pp. 3–4.

37 The extensive list of celluloid patents in Edward C. Worden, *Nitrocellulose Industry*, 2 vols. (New York: D. Van Nostrand, 1911), 2:773–92, includes these patents and many others.

38 Celluloid Manufacturing Co., "Licenses, Contracts & Patents 1872–1878," 2 vols., manuscript ledger held by the Celanese Plastics Co., Summit, N.J.

39 Worden, *Nitrocellulose*, 2:682–87.

40 Worden (ibid., pp. 687–97) describes these imitations and how they were made.

41 The Celluloid Mfg. Co. & The Piano Key Mfg. Co. v. The Pratt, Reed & Co. and The Comstock, Cheney & Co. (Circuit Court, District of Connecticut, in equity, 1882), case record held by the Celanese Plastics Co., Summit, N.J.

42 George F. Kunz, *Ivory and the Elephant in Art, in Archaeology, and in Science* (Garden City, N.Y.: Doubleday, Page & Co., 1916), p. 252.

43 Sears, Roebuck and Co., *Catalog* (Spring 1896), p. 511.

44 Masselon, Roberts, and Cillard, *Celluloid: Its Manufacture, Applications, and Substitutes*, trans. Herbert H. Hodgson (London: Chas. Griffin & Co., 1912), pp. 263–64.

Chapter 4: Applications, Impacts, and Images

1 U.S. Department of the Interior, Census Office, *Report on the Manufactures of the United States at the Tenth Census (June 1, 1880)* (Washington, D.C.: U.S. Government Printing Office, 1883), pp. 152 and 156.

2 U.S. Department of the Interior, Census Office, *Report on Manufacturing Industries in the United States at the Eleventh Census, 1890: Part I, Totals for States and Industries* (Washington, D.C.: U.S. Government Printing Office, 1895), pp. 154–55.

3 Edward C. Worden, *Nitrocellulose Industry*, 2 vols. (New York: D. Van Nostrand, 1911), 2:748–49.

4 Ibid.; Edward C. Worden, *Technology of Cellulose Esters*, 2 vols. (Easton, Pa.: Eschenbach Printing Co., 1921), 1:2667–68.

5 Before its demise, the American Zylonite Company copied the organizational strategy of the Celluloid Manufacturing Company. Thus, there was a Zylonite Brush and Comb Company (1883), a Zylonite Novelty Company (1884), and a Zylonite Collar and Cuff Company (1884).

6 Worden, *Cellulose Esters*, 1:2669–70.

7 Ibid., 1:1666–67; Worden, *Nitrocellulose*, 2:580.

8 "The Arlington Plant," *Du Pont Magazine* 9 (August 1918): 8–9; unsigned letter to Mr. Francis A. Gudger, 11 February 1916, in Jasper E. Crane Papers, Eleutherian Mills Historical Library, Greenville, Wilmington, Del.

9 "Minute Book, 7 December 1886–9 January 1892," Arlington Collar and Cuff Co., Records of E. I. du Pont de Nemours & Co., ser. II, p. 2, Eleutherian Mills Historical Library, Greenville, Wilmington, Del.

10 "Minute Book, 21 May 1886–10 April 1899," Arlington Co., Records of E. I. du Pont de Nemours, ser. II, p. 31; letter to Francis A. Gudger, Crane Papers.

11 Carl Marx, "The Rise of the First Great Plastic Industry," *Plastics* 4 (December 1928): 684.

12 Unsigned letter *re* collars, in Arlington Co., Records of E. I. du Pont de Nemours, ser. II.

13 "The Arlington Plant," pp. 8–9.

14 Morris Kaufman, *The First Century of Plastics* (London: The Plastics Institute, 1963), p. 41.

15 Worden, *Cellulose Esters*, 1:2668; Thomas Connolly, "Report on Caoutchouc," in *The Society of Arts Artisan Reports on the Paris Universal Exhibition of 1878* (London, 1879), p. 605.

16 Masselon, Roberts, and Cillard, *Celluloid: Its Manufacture, Applications, and Substitutes*, trans. Herbert H. Hodgson (London: Ch. Griffin & Co., 1912) p. 2.

17 Ibid.; Worden, *Nitrocellulose*, 2:573.

18 Worden, *Nitrocellulose*, 2:573; see also Josef Ertel, *Die volkwirtschaftliche Bedeutung der technischen Entwicklung der Zelluloidindustrie* (Leipzig: Verlag von Dr. Werner Klinkhardt, 1909), chap. 4.

19 Kaufman, *First Century*, pp. 41–44. Kaufman's chapters 5 and 6 are very good surveys of the spread of celluloid production in Europe.

20 Blanche Dominjon-Bombard, *Essai monographique sur Oyonnax et l'industrie du celluloid* (Lyon: Bosc Frères, 1935), pp. 27–28.

21 [Perry Walton], *Comb Making in America* (Boston: compiled and printed for Bernard W. Doyle, 1925), pp. 13–94 passim.

22 Ibid., pp. 138–40; Dominjon-Bombard, *Oyonnax*, p. 29.

23 Dominjon-Bombard, *Oyonnax*, pp. 30–31; Walton, *Comb Making*, pp. 48–75 passim.

24 "Patent Papers re Combs, 1814–1912," Arlington Co., Records of E. I. du Pont de Nemours, ser. II.

25 Walton, *Comb Making*, pp. 43–44.

26 William Booth, testimony in Daniel Spill, *appellant*, v. the Celluloid Manufacturing Company, U.S. Supreme Court, Appellate Case Files, no. 12305,
Record Group 267, National Archives, Washington, D.C., p. 1019. This is
Booth's identification of himself, given in testimony in 1880: "I am superinten-
dent of the Celluloid Brush Company. I have been so four or five years. I have
been engaged in the manufacture of articles of celluloid going on five years;
first in Leominster, Mass. I began there about five years ago—five years ago
next summer. The business in Massachusetts was that of manufacturing all
kinds of combs from celluloid."

27 It is not clear how important difficulties in acquiring horn were in the shift to
celluloid. Certainly, the price of horn combs in the 1890s did not reflect growing scarcity (see Table 3.4, above). On the other hand, it is possible that the
growing use of refrigeration, allowing local slaughtering in the Midwest to
replace shipment of live cattle to the East, separated the eastern combmakers
from their traditional sources of supply. If this was indeed a factor, it was a
remarkable example of the secondary effects of technological change.

28 Walton, *Comb Making*, pp. 114-16.

29 Dominjon-Bombard, *Oyonnax*, p. 41.

30 Kaufman, *First Century*, pp. 45-46.

31 Frank H. Pope, "Leominster's Lesson to the Growing Cities of
Massachusetts," *New England Magazine* 39 (February 1909): 717.

32 John J. Keville, "The History of Plastics in Leominster," *Industry*
(Massachusetts), July 1968, p. 16; Glenn D. Kittler, *"More than Meets the
Eye": The Foster Grant Story* (New York: Coronet Books, 1972).

33 A comparison of encyclopedia descriptions of Leominster and Oyonnax illustrates the changing identification of the towns. The 1875 edition of the
American Cyclopaedia (10:354) described Leominster as the "chief seat of the
comb manufacture of the state." The article on Leominster in the 1968 edition
of *Collier's Encyclopedia* (14:503), on the other hand, did not even mention
combmaking, stating simply that "plastics products constitute a major portion
of the city's manufactures." Similarly, the 1963 *Grand Larousse* (8:70) description of Oyonnax characterized the town as the "grand centre de l'industrie des
matières plastiques" and made no mention of combs.

34 *J. Soc. Arts* 19 (3 March 1871): 300.

35 Ibid. 24 (3 December 1875): 48.

36 *Scientific American* 40 (12 April 1879): 225; *English Mechanic* 29 (25 April
1879): 154; *Journal of the Franklin Institute* 107 (May 1879): 334-37; *Iron Age*
23 (22 May 1879): 7.

37 *Journal of the Franklin Institute* 108 (December 1879): 405-9; *Iron Age* 24 (25
December 1879): 13; *Popular Science Monthly* 16 (April 1880): 859-69; *New
York Times* 7 January 1880, p. 4.

38 Many of the same points in these articles were made in a more technical treatment that appeared in the *Moniteur Scientifique* 26 (1880): 696-99.

39 "The Philadelphia Novelties Exposition," *Frank Leslie's Illustrated
Newspaper* 61 (14 November 1885): 203.

40 *Journal of the Franklin Institute* 123 (February 1887): 156–57.

41 Ibid. 110 (October 1880): 281.

42 *Scientific American* 56 (29 January 1887): 69; also in *Iron Age* 39 (17 March 1887): 9.

43 Flammability was a deterrent to celluloid's adoption by printers. A number of histories of printing processes mention the use of celluloid, point out the claimed advantages of its use, and then, without giving specific reasons, state that celluloid actually was used very little and was quickly discarded. This was apparently due to the conservatism of printers rather than to technological competition. See George A. Kubler, *A New History of Stereotyping* (New York: Certified Dry Mat Corporation, 1941), pp. 84–88, and L. A. Legros and J. C. Grant, *Typographical Printing Surfaces* (London: Longmans, Green and Co., 1916), pp. 476–77.

44 *Scientific American* 56 (29 January 1887): 69.

45 From a Celluloid Manufacturing Company advertising card in the Warshaw Collection of Business Americana, Box "Collars and Cuffs," National Museum of American History, Smithsonian Institution, Washington, D.C.

46 *The Haberdasher*, vols. 22 (1895), 53 (1911), and 73 (1921); *Clothiers' and Haberdashers' Weekly*, vol. 6 (1895); *The Clothier and Furnisher*, vols. 10 (1880–81) and 25 (1895–96); and *Apparel Gazette (1902)*.

47 See also Kaufman, *First Century*, pp. 41 and 47.

48 Chauncey M. Depew, ed., *One Hundred Years of American Commerce, 1795–1895*, 2 vols. (New York: D. O. Haynes & Co., 1895), 2:668.

49 U.S. Department of Commerce and Labor, Bureau of the Census, *Manufactures, 1905, Part I: United States by Industries* (Washington, D.C.: U.S. Government Printing Office, 1907), pp. ccxxxv–ccxxxvi.

50 Celluloid Manufacturing Company, "Licenses, Contracts & Patents 1872–1878," 2 vols., manuscript ledger held by Celanese Plastics Company, Summit, N.J.

51 From *Chamber's Journal* (1896), quoted in Richard Corson, *Fashions in Eyeglasses* (Chester Springs, Pa.: Dufour, 1967), p. 138.

52 Corson, *Eyeglasses*, pp. 204–6.

53 *Ivaleur: A Sales Manual* (New York: The Celluloid Company, 1919), pp. 4–5.

54 Russell Lynes, *The Tastemakers* (New York: Grosset & Dunlap, 1954), esp. chap. 13.

55 G. H. Nevius, "Development in Popularity of White Ivory Toilet Goods," *Toilet Requisites* 1 (September 1916): 7–8.

56 These examples, as well as the figures, come from Pyralin (Arlington—Du Pont) catalogs of the 1920s. The articles offered in Ivaleur (Celluloid Company) were substantially the same.

57 Charles L. Eastlake, *Hints on Household Taste* (Boston: James R. Osgood & Co., 1872); Lynes, *Tastemakers*, chap. 7.

Chapter 5: Culmination and Consequences

1 Daniel Spill, "On Xylonite, a Material Applicable to Photographic Purposes," *British Journal of Photography* 17 (23 December 1870): 604.

2 For one of the reprints, see "The Uses of Celluloid," *English Mechanic* 29 (25 April 1879): 154. I have been unable to find the original *Evening Post* article.

3 E.g., J. Carbutt, "A Perfect Substitute for Glass as a Support for Gelatine Bromide of Silver for Use in Photography," *Journal of the Franklin Institute* 126 (December 1888): 478–82; "Celluloid," *British Journal of Photography* 36 (19 July 1889): 469–70 (reprinted in *Scientific American* 61 [31 August 1889]: 129).

4 W. Jerome Harrison, "Celluloid Films for the Lantern," *British Journal of Photography* 36 (13 December 1889): 813–14.

5 "Celluloid in Drawing," *Scientific American* 63 (8 November 1890): 292.

6 Reese V. Jenkins, *Images and Enterprise: Technology and the American Photographic Industry, 1839 to 1925* (Baltimore: Johns Hopkins University Press, 1975), p. 99n; Helmut Gernsheim, *The History of Photography* (New York: McGraw-Hill, 1969), pp. 405–8.

7 Gernsheim, *History of Photography*, pp. 405–6.

8 Jenkins, *Images and Enterprise*, pp. 96–106.

9 Ibid., pp. 108–12.

10 Ibid., pp. 112–20.

11 Ibid., pp. 127–29.

12 Edward C. Worden, *Nitrocellulose Industry*, 2 vols. (New York: D. Van Nostrand, 1911), 1:300. This was covered by U.S. Patent 269,340.

13 This also included the discovery of the usefulness of fusel oil, added to the film composition to preserve the clarity and surface of the film. Ibid., 2:847.

14 Jenkins, *Images and Enterprise*, pp. 129–32 and 332–34.

15 Ibid., chap. 12; Kenneth Macgowan, *Behind the Screen* (New York: Delacorte Press, 1965), chap. 4.

16 Thus, among the books about the movies that appeared between 1931 and 1974 were *The Celluloid Asylum*, *The Celluloid Curriculum*, *The Celluloid Literature*, *The Celluloid Muse*, *Celluloid Rock*, *The Celluloid Sacrifice*, and *The Celluloid Weapon*.

17 Carl Marx, "The Rise of the First Great Plastic Industry," *Plastics* 4 (December 1928): 670.

18 Jenkins, *Images and Enterprise*, p. 138.

19 Stevens and Lefferts of the Celluloid Company were credited with developing machinery for producing continuous celluloid film (U.S. Patent 573,928, issued in 1896), but they soon sold their patent to Eastman. See Worden, *Nitrocellulose*, 2:852 and J. Harry DuBois, *Plastics History U.S.A.* (Boston: Cahners Books, 1972), pp. 49–51.

20 *New York Times*, 16 September 1875, p. 4.

21 E.g., British Patent 2,359 of 1855. It was very early recognized that the addition of pigments and fillers to nitrocellulose plastics slowed down the burning of the material.

22 *Newark News*, 26 June 1949, clipping in the files of the Newark Public Library.

23 Josef Ertel, *Die volkwirtschaftliche Bedeutung der technischen Entwicklung der Zelluloidindustrie* (Leipzig: Verlag von Dr. Werner Klinkhardt, 1909), pp. 80–81.

24 *New York Times*, 19 September 1875, p. 7.

25 *New York Times*, 27 June 1878, p. 4.

26 Celluloid Manufacturing Company, "Scrapbook," held by Celanese Plastics Company, Chatham, N.J.

27 "Celluloid" (three boxes), Charles F. Chandler Papers, Columbia University.

28 Frank Vanderpoel, "Personal Reminiscences," *Journal of Industrial and Engineering Chemistry* 6 (February 1914): 161.

29 *Scientific American* 66 (2 April 1892): 208.

30 Ibid. 66 (23 April 1892): 261.

31 Great Britain, Home Department, *Report of the Departmental Committee on Celluloid* (London: H.M.S.O., 1913).

32 Ibid., p. 4.

33 Celluloid Manufacturing Company, "Scrapbook," partially identified clipping, no date.

34 Worden, *Nitrocellulose*, 2:762–63.

35 Masselon, Roberts, and Cillard, *Celluloid: Its Manufacture, Applications, and Substitutes*, trans. Herbert H. Hodgson (London: Ch. Griffin & Co., 1912), p. 339.

36 "Artificial Ivory," *The Engineer* 72 (16 October 1891): 311.

37 F. P. Pondorf, "Remarkable Rise of the Button Industry," *Plastics* 3 (June 1927): 270.

38 Gilbert T. Morgan and David D. Pratt, *British Chemical Industry: Its Rise and Development* (New York: Longmans, Green & Co., 1938), pp. 196–97.

39 Worden, *Nitrocellulose*, 2:1055–1110.

40 Ibid., Chap. 19; Edward C. Worden, *Technology of Cellulose Esters*, 2 vols. (Easton, Pa.: Eschenbach Printing Co., 1921), chaps. 1 and 4; Emil Ott, "Cellulose Derivatives as Basic Materials for Plastics," *Journal of Industrial and Engineering Chemistry* 32 (December 1940): 1642.

41 Aaron J. Ihde, *The Development of Modern Chemistry* (New York: Harper & Row, 1964), pp. 164–65.

42 Ibid., pp. 330–33.

43 The story of the beginnings of the synthetic dye industry has been told by a number of authors. The most useful here have been R. E. Rose, "Growth of the Dyestuffs Industry: The Application of Science to Art," *Journal of Chemical Education* 3 (September 1926): 973–78; John J. Beer, *The Emergence of the German Dye Industry*, Illinois Studies in the Social Sciences, vol. 44 (Urbana: University of Illinois Press, 1959), chaps. 1 and 3; R. D. Welham, "Early History of the Synthetic Dye Industry," *Journal of the Society of Dyers and Colorists* 79 (March 1963): 98–105, 79 (April 1963): 146–52, 79 (May 1963): 181–85, and 79 (June 1963): 229–37.

44 Beer, *German Dye Industry*, chaps. 6, 7, and 8; Ihde, *Modern Chemistry*, pp. 454–64.

45 Carl B. Kaufmann, "Grand Duke, Wizard, and Bohemian: A Biographical Profile of Leo Hendrik Baekeland" (M.A. thesis, University of Delaware, n.d.), chap. 2. The precise amount Baekeland received for Velox is reported

differently by other authors; see, for example, Williams Haynes, *This Chemical Age* (New York: Alfred A. Knopf, 1942), p. 338.

46 W. Kleeberg, "Ueber die Entwicklung des Formaldehyds auf Phenole," *Justus Liebigs Annalen der Chemie* 263 (1891): 284.

47 Leo H. Baekeland, "Bakelite, A New Composition of Matter: Its Synthesis, Constitution, and Uses," *Scientific American Supplement* 68 (20 November 1909): 322.

48 Kaufmann, "Baekeland," p. 99.

49 Leo H. Baekeland, "Laboratory Notebooks—BKL," 16 vols., 1:1, Leo Baekeland Papers, Division of Physical Sciences, National Museum of American History, Smithsonian Institution, Washington, D.C.

50 Ibid., pp. 10–11.

51 Ibid., pp. 12–13.

52 Ibid., pp. 16–17.

53 Ibid., pp. 13–14.

54 Leo H. Baekeland, "Diaries," 1 (3 April 1907–2 January 1908): 45–47, Baekeland Papers.

55 Baekeland, "Bakelite," p. 342.

56 DuBois, *Plastics History U.S.A.*, p. 99.

57 Baekeland, "Bakelite," pp. 342–43.

58 John K. Mumford, *The Story of Bakelite* (New York: Robert L. Stillson, 1924), p. 22.

59 See William S. Dutton, *Du Pont: One Hundred and Forty Years* (New York: Charles Scribner's Sons, 1942), p. 323.

60 Ott, "Cellulose Derivatives," p. 1642.

61 Great Britain, Home Department, *Report of the Departmental Committee on the Use of Celluloid in the Manufacture of Toys, Fancy Goods, Etc.* (London: H.M.S.O., 1938), pp. 3–4.

62 *Newark News*, 26 June 1949.

63 See British Industrial Plastics Limited, *Beetle Bulletin* 36 (n.d.): 9.

Conclusion

1 Emil Ott, "Cellulose Derivatives as Basic Materials for Plastics," *Journal of Industrial and Engineering Chemistry* 32 (December 1940): 1642.

2 P. Schidrowitz and T. R. Dawson, eds., *History of the Rubber Industry* (Cambridge: W. Heffer & Sons, 1952), p. 334.

A Note on Sources

THE HISTORY of celluloid can be documented through many kinds of sources upon which historians routinely rely—manuscript collections, periodical literature, and specialized histories of related subjects. In the case of celluloid, however, some of the key primary sources that would normally be used for a history such as this one do not exist. None of the principals involved in the invention of nitrocellulose plastics are known to have left collections of the sorts of papers and memorabilia that historians and biographers generally rely upon to understand the careers of inventors or the processes of invention itself. The Celluloid Company's own records of its first decades of business do not seem to have survived the merging of corporate staffs, the closing down of factories, and the eventual disappearance of both the company name and its product. A few odd scrapbooks and ledgers put away in research libraries of the Celanese Corporation are all that can be found from those early years. To fill in some important gaps in documenting both the invention of celluloid and the early experiences of the material in the marketplace, I have turned to two sources which I might otherwise not have resorted to, but which turned out to be of enormous value. In the belief that it might enhance the reader's understanding of the role these records play in this work and, further, that it might direct scholars with similar problems to some fruitful resources, a brief discussion follows of these sources.

Patent Litigation Records. Numerous patent cases were fought over the invention and use of celluloid. Only one of these was of great importance, however—that filed by Daniel Spill against the Celluloid Manufacturing Company in 1875. *Spill* v. *The Celluloid Manufacturing Company* dealt with the issues of what celluloid was, when it was invented, and by whom; thus the records of the case are of particular value in understanding the origins of celluloid. The case lasted fourteen years, ending in 1890 with the dismissal of Spill's appeal by the U.S. Supreme Court, due to his death. During this time several decisions were rendered in the case by Samuel Blatchford, first as judge of the U.S. Circuit Court for the Southern District of New York and later as a Justice of the U.S. Supreme Court. The most important of Blatchford's decisions are found in the *Federal Reporter* at the following locations: 2 (May–July 1880): 707-12; 10 (February-

April 1882) : 290–91; and 21 (August–November 1884) : 631–40. The first of these was the original finding for Daniel Spill, handed down 25 May 1880 and sometimes cited as 18 Blatchford C.C. 190. Blatchford's reversal and final rejection of Spill's suit was handed down 21 August 1884 and may be cited as 22 Blatchford C.C. 441. Blatchford was the most highly regarded patent judge of his time, and thus his decisions themselves are worthy of some consideration by the historian.

The material related to *Spill* v. *The Celluloid Manufacturing Company* used in this study came from two sources. The first, from the record of the original suit, was found in the documents of the U.S. Circuit Court for the Southern District of New York. The most important document here was the hand transcription of depositions filed under docket number 7-336 in the "Old Equity Case Files, 1846–1877," in Record Group 21, National Archives, Washington National Records Center, Suitland, Maryland. This consists of sworn depositions on the case taken before a U.S. Commissioner in London between 16 July 1878 and 30 September 1879. It includes testimony taken from Alexander Parkes, Daniel Spill, and others connected with the manufacture of parkesine and xylonite. Because the transcript consists of loosely bound, unnumbered pages, citations from this source are by the numbers assigned to the questions and answers cited. These numbers constitute a series only for the testimony of a particular witness; thus Question 14 for, say, Daniel Spill, bears no relationship to Question 14 for Alexander Parkes. A number with an X indicates testimony taken under cross-examination. In addition to the depositions taken in London, these records also include some exhibits submitted at the time, and these are cited as exhibits. Among these, it should be noted, was a small piece of parkesine, made to imitate malachite, submitted as an example of the material Alexander Parkes put on display at the London Exhibition of 1862 (and thus probably the oldest piece of plastic in America).

The second source provided by the case of *Spill* v. *The Celluloid Manufacturing Company* was the printed transcript of the case prepared for the Supreme Court appeal that Spill filed 16 October 1886. This is lodged under case number 12305 in the "U.S. Supreme Court Appellate Case Files," in Record Group 267, National Archives, Washington, D.C. The most important item here is a paperbound book of well over a thousand numbered pages constituting the bulk of testimony and exhibits taken in the case. Material from this book has been cited by page number. Not only do depositions and courtroom testimony appear here, but much else besides, including copies of many American and British patents submitted as evidence.

The most valuable item in the Supreme Court record, however, is what has been cited here as the "Master's Report." As a result of Judge Blatchford's original finding against the Celluloid Manufacturing Company, a master was appointed by the court in June 1880 to determine what damages were to be awarded Spill. The master's determination was based on the performance and profitability of the Celluloid Manufacturing Company before 1880. Hence, this report consisted of much evidence taken from the company regarding its first ten years in business. Since it was in the company's interest in these proceedings to understate its success, there was a bias built into the evidence submitted to the master. Nonetheless, the company could not grossly distort the record of its performance; thus this material remains a particularly valuable resource for understanding the commercial history of celluloid's first decade.

For the record, some of the other cases of interest concerning celluloid were *The Celluloid Manufacturing Company & The Piano Key Manufacturing Company* v. *Pratt, Reed & Company and Comstock, Cheney & Company*, U.S. Circuit Court for the District of Connecticut, 1882; *Celluloid Manufacturing Company* v. *American Zylonite Company, et al.*, U.S. Circuit Court for the Southern District of New York, 1886; and *Celluloid Manufacturing Company* v. *Cellonite Manufacturing Company*, U.S. Circuit Court for the Southern District of New York, 1890.

Credit Reporting Records. The other unusual source I turned to for documenting the experiences of the Celluloid Manufacturing Company in its first decades were credit-rating records. The archives of America's premier credit reporting agency, Dun and Bradstreet, have been preserved and are available to scholars in the Manuscripts Department of Harvard Business School's Baker Library, in Boston. The hundreds of oversize ledgers in which were recorded the observations of field agents constitute a matchless collection of eyewitness accounts of American commerce. In the 1850s, the Mercantile Agency, founded by Lewis Tappan, came under the ambitious direction of Robert G. Dun, who expanded the services of the company to cover every part of the United States and several foreign countries. Dun organized a network of investigators who would, as the need arose or opportunities presented themselves, make discreet inquiries about the nature of businesses, their profitability, their borrowing habits, and any other matter that might be of interest to lenders. In the case of new businesses, investigators would often make a point of learning more about the workings of the enterprise and how well it was being received. The records of R. G. Dun and Company (as it was known until 1933) are therefore particularly rich in information on struggling new companies in their first years—just the period when a company's internal records may be most unreliable or most likely to be lost.

The excerpts from the Dun and Company agents' reports on the Celluloid Manufacturing Company that are used in chapter three of this work are good examples of the kind of information that these records provide. The observations made by these agents are sometimes the only reliable eyewitness commentary that can be found concerning the early years of such companies. The agents' observations were confidential; the only information that reached Dun's customers were the letter-and-number credit ratings that were published several times a year in the *Mercantile Agency Reference Book*, sent out to subscribers of the rating service. The ratings themselves, surveyed over a number of years, can provide a picture of a company's growth. In the case of celluloid, owing to the numerous small fabricating companies, a general picture of the whole industry can be gleaned from the credit ratings. The accompanying table gives the results of a survey of the ratings given for the Celluloid Manufacturing Company and the fabricating companies between 1875 and 1900. The letter part of the rating code, which ranged generally upward from *G* to *A* (later, *AA*), referred to the relative size of the con-

Credit Ratings of the Celluloid Manufacturing Company and Related Companies,
from Dun, Barlow & Company (later R. G. Dun & Company)
Mercantile Agency Reference Book

	1875	1880	1883	1885	1890	1895	1900
Celluloid Manufacturing Co.	C 2	C 1½	B + 1	B + 1	A A1	AA A1*	AA A1*
Celluloid Harness Trimming Co.	F 3	dropped					
Celluloid Brush Co.		C 2	B 1	B 1	B 1½	dropped	
Celluloid Emery Wheel Co.		**	**	dropped			
Celluloid Novelty Co.		F 3	D 2	B 1	B 1	dropped	
Celluloid Piano Key Co.		F 3	F 3	F 3	F 3	F 3	F 3
Celluloid Shoe Protector Co.		3½	dropped				
Celluloid Waterproof Cuff & Collar Co.		G 3	G 3	G 3	dropped		
Celluloid Corset & Clasp Co.			**	dropped			
Celluloid Showcase Co.			C 1½	C 1½	C 1½	dropped	
Celluloid Stereotype Co.			F 3	F 3	dropped		
Celluloid Surgical Instrument Co.			F 3	dropped			
Celluloid Varnish Co.					E 2	dropped	
Celluloid Enamel Co.					**	dropped	
Celluloid Zapon Co. (varnishes)						3	dropped

*Rated as the Celluloid Company.
**Not rated, but listed.

cern being rated ("pecuniary strength" in Dun's terms). The actual correspondence of the letters to figures representing total assets changed through the years and, in fact, is often not reported in the *Reference Book;* hence the ratings cannot reliably be used to determine the assets of companies, but they still give a good picture of the growth of assets over time. The numerical ratings, ranging from $3\frac{1}{2}$ to 1 (later, *A* 1), refer to general creditworthiness: $3\frac{1}{2}$ was the low end of "fair" and 1 was the best possible. Sometimes a company would be listed, but not given a rating; this might mean that there was not enough information to allow any ratings to be given, but it might also mean that the company's creditworthiness was open to question and should be looked at closely by any prospective lender. The modest and often precarious nature of the celluloid fabricating companies is well reflected by their ratings during this period, and they contrast markedly with the steady progress of the celluloid manufacturers themselves, from a lowly *C* 2 rating in 1875 to the pinnacle of *AA A* 1 twenty years later.

Bibliography

Manuscript Sources

Leo H. Baekeland Papers. National Museum of American History. Smithsonian Institution. Washington, D.C.

Celanese Plastics Company. Chatham and Summit, N.J.

Charles F. Chandler Collection. Columbia University Library. New York, N.Y.

Jasper E. Crane Papers. Eleutherian Mills Historical Library. Greenville, Wilmington, Del.

Records of R. G. Dun & Company. Baker Library. Harvard University Graduate School of Business Administration. Boston, Mass.

Records of E. I. du Pont de Nemours & Company. Series II: Absorbed Companies. Eleutherian Mills Historical Library. Greenville, Wilmngton, Del.

Printed Miscellany

Warshaw Collection of Business Americana. National Museum of American History. Smithsonian Institution. Washington, D.C.

Catalogs

Albany Billiard Ball Company. *Hyatt Patent Billiard and Pool Balls.* Albany, N.Y., 1899.

[B.] Altman & Company. *Catalogue.* New York, Fall–Winter 1882–83, Fall–Winter 1888–89, Fall–Winter 1892–93, Spring–Summer 1912.

The Celluloid Company. *Catalogue 117.* [Newark, N.J. ?], [1920 ?].

[E. I.] du Pont de Nemours & Co. *Pyralin Toiletware.* New York, 1922, 1926.

Ehrich & Company [later Ehrich Brothers]. *Ehrich Fashion Quarterly.* New York, Summer 1877, Fall 1879, Fall 1881, Fall 1885.

[Augustus] Ferschke. *Catalogue* (barbers' supplies). Wilmington, Del., [1890s ?].

Heinr. ad. Meyer. *Ivory.* Hamburg, 1876.

Lynch & Company. *Catalogue and Illustrations of Druggists' Sundries and Surgical Instruments.* London, January 1889.

137

Spelman Brothers. *Fancy Goods Graphic.* New York, September 1883, July 1885,
   November 1885, December 1885, December 1887, January 1888, February
   1888, March 1888, August 1888, October 1888, December 1888, July 1889.
[George] Wright & Company. *Eburnea, the Synthetic Ivory* (for billiards). London, [1891–92 ?].

Trade Journals

Apparel Gazette [later *Chicago Apparel Gazette*], vol. 25 (1902).
The Clothier & Furnisher (New York), vols. 10–12 (1880–82), 24 (1894).
The Clothiers' and Haberdashers' Weekly (New York, vol. 3 (1893–94).
The Haberdasher (New York), vol. 11 (1890).

Published Sources

Addis, Robert. "The History of the Toothbrush." *British Dental Journal* 66
   (1939): 532–33.
Angus, Robert. "Whatever Happened to Pure Virgin Vinyl? Why Records are
   Black." *Forecast!* February 1975, pp. 60–61.
"Applications of Celluloid." *Scientific American* 40 (12 April 1879): 225.
"The Arlington Plant." *DuPont Magazine* 9 (August 1918): 8–9.
"Artificial Ivory." *The Engineer* 72 (16 October 1891): 311–12.
"Artificial Ivory." *Journal of the Society of Arts* 14 (1 December 1865): 45.
"An Artificial Ivory." *Journal of the Society of Arts* 14 (16 November 1866):
   782–83.
"Artificial Ivory." *Scientific American* 64 (31 January 1891): 73.
"Artificial Ivory." *Scientific American* 65 (12 September 1891): 167.
"Artificial Ivory." *Scientific American* 67 (17 September 1892): 186.
"Aus der Praxis der Celluloidwarenfabrikation." *Gummi-Zeitung* 14 (1900):
   19–20.
Baekeland, Leo H. "Bakelite, A New Composition of Matter: Its Synthesis, Con-
   stitution, and Uses." *Scientific American Supplement* 68 (November 1909):
   322–23, 342–43.
Baekeland, Leo H. "The Invention of Celluloid." *Journal of Industrial and
   Engineering Chemistry* 6 (1914): 90–91.
Barker, P. W. *Charles Goodyear: Connecticut Yankee and Rubber Pioneer.*
   Boston: Godfrey L. Cabot, 1940.
Beer, John J. *The Emergence of the German Dye Industry.* Illinois Studies in the
   Social Sciences, vol. 44. Urbana: University of Illinois Press, 1959.
Bersch, Joseph. *Cellulose, Cellulose Products, and Artificial Rubber.* Translated
   by W. T. Brannt. Philadelphia: Henry Carey Baird & Co., 1904.
Bishop, P. W. "John Wesley Hyatt and the Discovery of Celluloid." *Plastics
   World*, October 1968, pp. 30–38.
Blau, Hans. "Hundert Jahre Konsumguter aus Kunstoffen." In *Die
   Verarbeitung von Kunstoffen in Gegenwart und Zukunft*, edited by Reinmar
   Furst, pp. 99–106. Dusseldorf: Econ Verlag, 1974.

Bockmann, Friedrich. *Celluloid: Its Raw Material, Manufacture, Properties, and Uses.* . . . Translated by Charles Salter. London: Scott, Greenwood & Son, 1907. Original German edition, Vienna, A. Hartleberg Verlag, 1880.

Boehmer, George H. "Celluloid: Grand-daddy of 'em All." *Modern Plastics* 12 (September 1934): 46–51, 66, 80.

Bonwitt, Gustav. *Das Celluloid und seine Ersatzstoffe.* Berlin: Union Deutsche Verlagsgesellschaft, 1933.

Brown, E. R. "Collars." *DuPont Magazine* 8 (June 1918): 7.

Buttrey, Douglas N. *Cellulose Plastics.* London: Cleaver-Hume Press, [1947].

Carbutt, Jno. "A Perfect Substitute for Glass as a Support for Gelatine Bromide of Silver for Use in Photography." *Journal of the Franklin Institute* 126 (December 1888): 478–82.

Cassell's Illustrated Family Paper Exhibitor. London: Cassell, Petter & Galpin, 1862.

"Celluloid." *British Journal of Photography* 36 (19 July 1889): 469–70.

"Celluloid." *Iron Age* 23 (22 May 1879): 7.

"Celluloid." *Journal of the Franklin Institute* 107 (May 1879): 334–37.

"Celluloid." *Journal of the Society of Arts* 24 (3 December 1875): 48.

"Celluloid." *Journal of the Society of Chemical Industry* 10 (30 June 1891): 564–65.

"Le Celluloid." *Moniteur Scientifique* 26 (1880): 696–99.

"Celluloid." *Nature* 22 (19 August 1880): 370–71.

"Celluloid." *Scientific American* 61 (31 August 1889): 129.

The Celluloid Company. *Celluloid: How Celluloid Is Made.* [Newark, N.J.?, n.d.]

The Celluloid Company. *Ivaleur: A Sales Manual.* New York: The Celluloid Company, 1919.

"A Celluloid Composition for Driving Belts for Machinery." *Journal of the Franklin Institute* 146 (December 1898): 476.

"The Celluloid Explosion." *New York Times,* 19 September 1875, p. 7.

"Celluloid, First Made Commercial Success in Newark. . . ." *Newark Evening News,* 7 February 1917, p. 14.

"Celluloid in Drawing." *Scientific American* 63 (8 November 1890): 292.

"Celluloid is one of the most remarkable. . . ." *New York Times,* 7 January 1880, p. 4.

"Celluloid Litigation." *Scientific American* 63 (2 August 1890): 73.

Celluloid Manufacturing Company. *Celluloid as a Base for Artificial Teeth.* New York: Celluloid Manufacturing Co., 1878.

"Celluloid Stereotypes." *Journal of the Franklin Institute* 110 (October 1880): 281.

Chandler, Charles F. "The Invention of Celluloid." *Journal of Industrial and Engineering Chemistry* 6 (July 1914): 601–2.

Chandler, Charles F. "Presentation Address." *Journal of Industrial and Engineering Chemistry* 6 (February 1914): 156–58.

Coleman, Donald C. *Courtauld's: An Economic and Social History.* Oxford: Clarendon Press, 1969.

"Composition and Uses of Celluloid." *The Popular Science Monthly* 16 (April 1880): 859–60.

Connolly, Thomas. "Report on Caoutchouc." *The Society of Arts Artisan Reports on the Paris Universal Exhibition of 1878.* London, 1879.

Cook, J. Gordon. *The Miracle of Plastics.* New York: Dial Press, 1964.

Corson, Richard. *Fashions in Eyeglasses.* Chester Springs, Pa.: Dufour, 1967.

"Dangers of Celluloid." *Scientific American* 66 (2 April 1892): 208.

"Death of Mr. Alexander Parkes." *Engineering* 50 (25 July 1890): 111.

Delorme, Jean, and Laroux, Pierre. *Les Conquêtes des matières plastiques en médecine et en chirurgie.* Casablanca: Les Editions Amphora, 1950.

The Dental Cosmos: A Monthly Report of Dental Science. Philadelphia: Samuel S. White, 1871 (vol. 13), 1873 (vol. 15), and 1874 (vol. 16). Advertising sections only (bound separately).

Depew, Chauncey M., ed. *One Hundred Years of American Commerce, 1795–1895.* 2 vols. New York: D. O. Haynes & Co., 1895.

Dhommée, René. "Fabrication du Celluloid." *La Revue Technique* 26 (10 May 1905): 372–73.

Dick, William B. *Dick's Encyclopedia of Practical Receipts and Processes.* Edited by Leicester and Harriet Handsfield. New York: Funk & Wagnalls, 1975. Reprinted from an unspecified edition of the 1870s.

Dominjon-Bombard, Blanche. *Essai Monographique sur Oyonnax el l'Industrie du Celluloid.* Lyon: Bosc Frères, 1935.

DuBois, J. Harry. *Plastics History U.S.A.* Boston: Cahners Books, 1972.

Dutton, William S. *Du Pont: One Hundred and Forty Years.* New York: Charles Scribner's Sons, 1942.

Eastlake, Charles L. *Hints on Household Taste.* Boston: James R. Osgood & Co., 1872.

Eder, Josef Maria. *History of Photography.* New York: Dover Publications, 1948, 1978.

"Einiges aus der Geschichte der Celluloid-Industrie." *Gummi-Zeitung* 14 (September 1900): 845–47.

Emmerson, Donald W. *Canadian Inventors and Innovators: Pioneering in Plastics.* Scarborough, Ont.: Canadian Plastics Pioneers, [1978].

"Der Erfinder des Zelluloids." *Kunstoffe* 4 (1 December 1914): 383–84.

"Die Erfindung des Zelluloids." *Kunstoffe* 4 (15 July 1914): 275–77.

Ertel, Josef. *Die volkwirtschaftliche Bedeutung der technischen Entwicklung der Zelluloidindustrie.* Leipzig: Verlag von Dr. Werner Klinkhardt, 1909.

"Experiments with Celluloid." *Scientific American* 66 (23 April 1892): 261.

"Explosive Teeth." *New York Times,* 16 September 1875, p. 4.

Faraday, Michael. *The Letters of Faraday and Schönbein, 1836–1862.* Edited by Georg W. A. Kahlbaum and Francis V. Darbishire. Basel and London: Williams & Norgate, 1899.

Ford, William F. *The Industrial Interests of Newark, N.J.* New York: Van Arsdale & Co., 1874.

Gernsheim, Helmut. *The History of Photography.* New York: McGraw-Hill, 1969.

Gibson, Reginald O. *The Discovery of Polythene.* Royal Institute of Chemistry, Lecture Series, 1964, no. 1. London: Royal Institute of Chemistry, 1964.

Glanville, A.B. "Plastics and Society." *Plastics and Polymers* 41 (October 1973): 242–48.

Goodyear, Charles. *Gum-elastic and its Varieties, with a Detailed Account of its Applications and Uses, and of the Discovery of Vulcanization.* 2 vols. New Haven: for the author, 1853–55.

Great Britain. Home Department. *Report of the Departmental Committee on Celluloid.* London: HMSO, 1913.

Great Britain, Home Department. *Report of the Departmental Committee on the Use of Celluloid in the Manufacture of Toys, Fancy Goods, etc.* London: HMSO, 1938.

Greenfield, Julia. "With the Pioneers, II: Alexander Parkes and Parkesine." *Plastics* 2 (February 1926): 49–50, 60.

"Gun Cotton Ivory." *Journal of the Society of Arts* 19 (3 March 1871): 300.

Harrison, W. Jerome. "Celluloid Films for the Lantern." *British Journal of Photography* 36 (13 December 1889): 813–14.

Haynes, Williams. *American Chemical Industry.* 6 vols. New York: D. Van Nostrand Co., 1954.

Haynes, Williams. *Cellulose, the Chemical That Grows.* New York: Doubleday & Co., 1953.

Haynes, Williams. *This Chemical Age: The Miracle of Man-Made Materials.* New York: Alfred A. Knopf, 1942.

Herrmannsdörfer, Helmut. *Geschichte und Entwicklung der dentalen Kunstoffe.* Munich: Institut für Geschichte der Medizin der Universität München, 1954.

Hogben, Walter. "The Properties and Manufacture of Celluloid." *Journal of Chemical Industry* 11 (31 March 1892): 222–24.

"How Celluloid Billiard Balls Are Manufactured." *Scientific American* 48 (19 May 1883): 306.

Hyatt, John Wesley. "Address of Acceptance" (of the Perkin Medal). *Journal of Industrial and Engineering Chemistry* 6 (February 1914): 158–61.

Ihde, Aaron J. *The Development of Modern Chemistry.* New York: Harper & Row, 1964.

International Labour Office. *Safety in the Manufacture and Use of Celluloid.* Studies and Reports, Series F, Second Section (Safety), no. 6. Geneva: ILO, 1933.

"The Ivory Trade." *Journal of the Society of Arts* 12 (5 February 1864): 190.

"The Ivory Trade." *Journal of the Society of Arts* 47 (25 November 1898): 38–39.

Jenkins, Reese V. *Images and Enterprise: Technology and the American Photographic Industry, 1839 to 1925.* Baltimore: Johns Hopkins University Press, 1975.

"John Wesley Hyatt, der Erfinder des Zelluloids." *Kunstoffe* 4 (1 May 1914): 171–72.

Johnson, Benjamin P. *Report on International Exhibition of Industry and Art, London, 1862* (Report of the U.S. commissioner). Albany: C. Van Benthuysen, 1863.

Joyce, C. M. Letter to the editor. *Journal of Industrial and Engineering Chemistry* 3 (September 1911): 702.

Katz, Sylvia. *Plastics Designs and Materials.* London: Studio Vista, [1978].

Kaufman, Morris. *The First Century of Plastics: Celluloid and Its Sequel.* London: The Plastics Institute, 1963.

Kaufmann, Carl B. "Grand Duke, Wizard, and Bohemian: A Biographical Profile of Leo Hendrik Baekeland (1863–1944)." M.A. thesis, University of Delaware, Newark, Del., n.d.

Kean, Sumner. *Mold of Fortune: Lionel B. Kavanagh and the First Half Century of Plastics.* Leominster, Mass.: (privately printed), [1959].

Keville, John J. "The History of Plastics in Leominster." *Industry* (Massachusetts), July 1968, pp. 15–16.

Kittler, Glenn D. *"More than Meets the Eye": The Foster Grant Story.* New York: Coronet Books, 1972.

Kleeberg, Werner. "Ueber die Einwirkung des Formaldehyds auf Phenole." *Justus Liebig's Annalen der Chemie* 263 (1891): 283–86; 264 (1891): 351.

Kline, Gordon M. "History of Plastics and Their Uses in the Automotive Industry." *Modern Plastics* 17 (July 1940): 49–53, 84–88.

Kubler, George A. *A New History of Stereotyping.* New York: Certified Dry Mat Corporation, 1941.

Kunz, George F. *Ivory and the Elephant in Art, in Archaeology, and in Science.* Garden City, N.Y.: Doubleday, Page & Co., 1916.

Legros, L. A., and Grant, J. C. *Typographical Printing-Surfaces.* London: Longmans, Green & Co., 1916.

Lock, C. G. W., ed. *Spon's Encyclopaedia of the Industrial Arts, Manufacture, and Raw Commercial Products.* 2 vols. London: E. & F. N. Spon, 1882.

London International Exhibition of 1862. *The Illustrated Catalogue of the Industrial Department: British Division.* London: for Her Majesty's Commissioners, [1862?].

Lynes, Russell. *The Tastemakers.* New York: Grosset & Dunlap, 1954.

Macgowan, Kenneth. *Behind the Screen.* New York: Delacorte Press, 1965.

Mallet, Robert. *The Record of the International 1862 Exhibition.* Glasgow: Wm. Mackenzie, [1862 ?].

"The Manufacture and Uses of Celluloid." *Iron Age* 24 (25 December 1879): 13.

"The Manufacture of Celluloid." *Scientific American* 45 (23 July 1881): 48–49.

"Manufacture of Celluloid." *Scientific American* 63 (16 August 1890): 106.

Marx, Carl. "Blood and Shellac Plastics Fifty Years Ago." *Plastics* 3 (September 1927): 462.

Marx, Carl. "The Rise of the First Great Plastic Industry." *Plastics* 4 (December 1928): 669–71, 684, 693–94.

Marx, Carl. "With the Pioneers, I: Schönbein, Discoverer of Cellulose Nitrate." *Plastics* 2 (January 1926): 9–10, 30–32.

Marx, Carl. "With the Pioneers, III: The Case of *Spill* vs. *The Celluloid Company.*" *Plastics* 2 (March 1926): 86, 97, 100.

Maskell, Alfred. "Ivory in Commerce and in the Arts." Cantor Lectures. *Journal of the Society of Arts* 54 (2 November 1906): 1127-42; 54 (9 November 1906): 1146-69; 54 (16 November 1906): 1174-83.

Masselon, _____; Roberts, _____; and Cillard, _____. *Celluloid: Its Manufacture, Applications, and Substitutes.* Translated by Herbert H. Hodgson. London: Ch. Griffin & Co., 1912; original French edition, Paris, 1910.

Matthis, Alfred R. *Leo H. Baekeland, 1863-1944: Professeur, Docteur en Sciences, Chimiste, Inventeur et grand Industriel.* Collection Nationale. Brussels: Office de Publicité, 1948.

Merriam, John. *Pioneering in Plastics.* Ipswich, Suffolk: East Anglian Magazine, 1976.

Morgan, Gilbert T., and Pratt, David D. *British Chemical Industry: Its Rise and Development.* New York: Longmans, Green & Co., 1938.

Mumford, John K. *The Story of Bakelite.* New York: Robert L. Stillson, 1924.

Neustatter, Otto. "A Lost Art in the Field of Plastics: Papier Mache. . . ." *Plastics* 3 (May 1927): 206-7. From *Kunstoffe* 17 (1927): 64.

Nevius, G. H. "Development in Popularity of White Ivory Toilet Goods." *Toilet Requisites* 1 (September 1916): 7-9, 24.

Obach, Eugene F. A. "Gutta Percha." Cantor Lectures. *Journal of the Society of Arts* 46 (24 December 1897): 97-114; 46 (31 December 1897): 117-133; 46 (7 January 1898): 137-64; 46 (14 January 1898): 169-97.

Ott, Emil. "Cellulose Derivatives as Basic Materials for Plastics." *Journal of Industrial and Engineering Chemistry* 32 (December 1940): 1641-47.

Owen, Richard. "The Ivory and Teeth of Commerce." *Journal of the Society of Arts* 5 (19 December 1856): 65-73.

Parkes, Alexander. *Brief Account of the Invention and Manufacture of Parkesine.* Birmingham: Corns and Bartleet, 1867.

Parkes, Alexander. "On the Properties of Parkesine and Its Application to the Arts and Manufactures." *Journal of the Society of Arts* 14 (22 December 1865): 81-86.

"Parkesine, Xylonite, or Celluloid." *Scientific American Supplement* 9 (8 May 1880): 3617.

"The Perkins-Hyatt (Celluloid) Base." *British Journal of Dental Science* 14 (1871): 364-68.

Phelan, Michael. *The Game of Billiards.* 4th ed. New York: D. Appleton & Co., 1859.

"The Philadelphia Novelties Exposition." *Frank Leslie's Illustrated Newspaper* 61 (14 November 1885): 203.

Pondorf, F. P. "Remarkable Rise of the Button Industry." *Plastics* 3 (May 1927): 210; 3 (June 1927): 270, 284-85.

Pope, Frank H. "Leominster's Lesson to the Growing Cities of Massachusetts." *New England Magazine* 38 (February 1909): 709-21.

"Presents." *New York Times,* 27 June 1878, p. 4.

Prothero, James H. *Prosthetic Dentistry.* Chicago: Medico-Dental Publishing Co., 1916.

"Py-ra-lin." *DuPont Magazine* 8 (January 1918): 7.

"Reports of the Committee on Science and the Arts." *Journal of the Franklin Institute* 123 (February 1887): 156–57.

Rinhart, Floyd, and Rinhart, Marion. *American Miniature Case Art.* South Brunswick, N.J.: A. S. Barnes & Co., 1969.

"A Rival to Celluloid." *Journal of the Franklin Institute* 150 (September 1900): 237–38.

Rockhill, V. C. "Looking Back." *Plastics* 3 (June 1927): 300.

Rose, R. E. "Growth of the Dyestuffs Industry: The Application of Science to Art." *Journal of Chemical Education* 3 (September 1926): 973–1007.

Ross, Ishbel. *Taste in America.* New York: Thomas Y. Crowell, 1967.

Routledge, Robert. *Discoveries and Inventions of the Nineteenth Century.* London: George Routledge & Sons, 1879.

Sadtler, Samuel P. "Celluloid." *Iron Age* 39 (17 March 1887): 9.

Sadtler, Samuel P. "Celluloid." *Scientific American* 56 (29 January 1887): 69.

"Scarcity of Ivory." *Journal of the Society of Arts* 30 (9 June 1882): 814.

Schidrowitz, P., and Dawson, T. R., eds. *History of the Rubber Industry.* Cambridge: W. Heffer & Sons, 1952.

Schüpphaus, Robert C. "Contributions of the Chemist to the Celluloid and Nitrocellulose Industry." *Journal of Industrial and Engineering Chemistry* 7 (April 1915): 290.

Schüpphaus, Robert C. "The Invention of Celluloid." *Journal of Industrial and Engineering Chemistry* 6 (May 1914): 440–41.

Seeligmann, T.; Torrilhon, G. Lamy; and Falconnet, H. *Indiarubber and Gutta Percha.* Translated by J. G. McIntosh. London: Scott, Greenwood & Co., 1903.

"Set Out to Make New Billiard Ball and Started a Great Industry." *Newark Call,* 3 August 1919.

Simmonds, P. L. "Our Supplies of Ivory." *Journal of the Society of Arts* 30 (29 September 1882): 1018–19.

Smith, Adele M. *Printing and Writing Materials: Their Evolution.* Philadelphia: by the author, 1901.

Smith, Cyril Stanley. "Materials and the Development of Civilization and Science." *Science* 148 (14 May 1965): 908–17.

Spill, Daniel. "On Xylonite, a Material Applicable to Photographic Purposes." *British Journal of Photography* 17 (23 December 1870): 603–4.

Stevens, John H. "In the Composition of 'Celluloid' Chemistry Has Exhibited One of Her Most Complete Triumphs." *Newark Sunday News,* 30 August 1903, sec. 2, p. 4.

Strauss, Victor. *The Printing Industry.* Washington: Printing Industries of America, 1967.

"The Supply of Ivory." *New York Times,* 7 July 1867, p. 3.

Taft, Robert. *Photography and the American Scene: A Social History, 1839–1889.* New York: Macmillan, 1938; reprint ed., New York: Dover, 1964.

Thompson, Gustave W. "Chairman's Address" (for Perkin Medal award). *Journal of Industrial and Engineering Chemistry* 6 (February 1914): 155–56.

Timbs, John. *The International Exhibition. The Industry, Science, & Art of the Age; or, The International Exhibition of 1862 Popularly Described.* . . . London: Lockwood & Co., 1863.

Turin, L. "Les Dérivés industriels de la Nitrocellulose: Le Celluloid." *Le Génie Civil* 44 (9 January 1904): 152–55; 44 (16 January 1904): 170–71; 44 (23 January 1904): 190–92.

"Two New Processes for Making Artificial Ivory." *Scientific American* 50 (2 February 1884): 71.

U.S. Department of Commerce. Bureau of the Census. *Biennial Census of Manufactures, 1921.* Washington: Government Printing Office, 1924.

U.S. Department of Commerce. Bureau of Economic Analysis. *Long-Term Economic Growth, 1860–1970.* Washington: Government Printing Office, 1973.

U.S. Department of Commerce and Labor. Bureau of the Census. *(Census of) Manufactures, 1905, Part I: U.S. by Industries.* Washington: Government Printing Office, 1907.

U.S. Department of the Interior. Census Office. *Report on the Manufactures of the United States at the Tenth Census (June 1, 1880).* Washington: Government Printing Office, 1883.

U.S. Department of the Interior. Census Office. *Report on Manufacturing Industries in the United States at the Eleventh Census, 1890, Part I: Totals for States and Industries.* Washington: Government Printing Office, 1895.

"The Uses of Celluloid." *The English Mechanic* 29 (25 April 1879): 154.

"The Utilization of Waste Ivory." *Scientific American* 44 (19 February 1881): 118.

Vanderpoel, Frank. "Personal Reminiscences" (of J. W. Hyatt). *Journal of Industrial and Engineering Chemistry* 6 (February 1914): 161–62.

Voigt, _____. "Celluloid." *Gummi-Zeitung* 13 (1899): 620–21. Also appears as "Zelluloid." *Zeitschrift des Vereins deutscher Ingenieure* 43 (6 May 1899): 524–25.

Wahl, W. H. "Celluloid: What It Is and How It Is Made." *Journal of the Franklin Institute* 108 (December 1879): 405–9. Also in *The Manufacturer and Builder* 12 (January 1880): 7.

Walton, Perry. *Comb Making in America: An Account of the Origin and Development of the Industry for Which Leominster has Become Famous.* Boston: compiled and printed for Bernard W. Doyle, 1925.

Worden, Edward C. "The Inventor of Celluloid." *Journal of Industrial and Engineering Chemistry* 3 (June 1911): 436–37.

Worden, Edward C. *Nitrocellulose Industry.* 2 vols. New York: D. Van Nostrand, 1911.

Worden, Edward C. *Technology of Cellulose Esters.* 2 vols. (styled vol. 1 and vol. 8). Easton, Pa.: Eschenbach Printing Co., 1921.

Worden, Edward C. *Technology of Cellulose Ethers.* 5 vols. Millburn, N.J.: Worden Laboratory and Library, 1933.

Index

Acetate. *See* Cellulose acetate

Acrylics, 39, 108

Advertisements: for celluloid dental plates, 37–38; for parkesine, 44, 47; for celluloid collars and cuffs, 78–84 *passim*

Albany Billiard Ball Company: use of celluloid, 35, 56; difficulties, 49; adopts Bakelite, 107

Albany Dental Plate Company: formed, 16; use of celluloid, 36; advertisements, 37–38; difficulties, 49

Alizarin, 102

(B.) Altman & Company, 63

Amber: celluloid imitation of, 61, 76, 86, 89; substitution for, 77

"American linen," 71

American Zylonite Company, 68, 69, 124n5

Amyl acetate, 93

Aniline dyes, 101

Archer, Frederick Scott, 5, 41–42

Archerotype, 5

Arlington Collar and Cuff Company, 69

Arlington Company: successor to Arlington Manufacturing Company, 69; price-fixing of combs, 70; purchased by Du Pont, 70, 109; mentioned, 84

Arlington Manufacturing Company, 69

Art: parkesine applied to, 45, 46; appeals to in celluloid advertising, 85, 86

Atlantic cable, 46

Baekeland, Leo Hendrick: on J. W. Hyatt, 29; background, 103; Velox, 103; laboratory work, 103–4; references to

celluloid, 104; invention of Bakelite, 105–6

Baeyer, Adolf von, 102, 104

Bagatelle balls, 48

Bakelite: in billiard balls, 36, 39; significance of, 103, 107–8, 110; discovery, 106; properties, 106–7; production, 107; sources of invention, 114; mentioned, 104

"Bakelizer," 107

Barlow, H. W., 26

Barnwell, Stephen, 12–13

Berliner, Emile, 28

Berthelot, Marcellin, 101

Bevan, Edward J., 99

Billiard balls: prize for ivory substitute, 13; object of Hyatt's work, 29; special requirements for, 34; manufacture, 34–35; parkesine proposed for, 43; use of celluloid, 55; Bakelite proposed for, 107; mentioned, 60, 65, 77, 109, 112. *See also* Ivory

Billiards, 68

Blair Camera Company, 95

Blatchford, Samuel, 131–32

Bookbinding: collodion applied to, 43; parkesine used for, 44, 46

Booth, William, 125n26

Braconnot, Henry, 4

Britain: celluloid manufacture, 70–71; "celluloid committee," 97-98

British Xylonite Company, 71

Brushes, 56

Buttons: collodion applied to, 43; parkesine used for, 44, 45;

147